BLITHE SPIRITS

Blithe Spirits

AN ANTHOLOGY OF

CATHOLIC HUMOR

★

EDITED BY

DAN HERR AND JOEL WELLS

★

CLARETIAN FATHERS
400 NORTH EUCLID AVENUE
OAK PARK, ILLINOIS

DOUBLEDAY & COMPANY, INC.
GARDEN CITY, NEW YORK

Grateful acknowledgment is made to the following for granting permission to reprint the selections which appear in this book:

BRANDT & BRANDT. "O'Halloran's Luck" from *Selected Works of Stephen Vincent Benét*. Holt, Rinehart & Winston, Inc. Copyright 1938 by Stephen Vincent Benét. Reprinted by permission of Brandt & Brandt.

JOE COOGAN. "Double Skull, Slow Burn, and a Ping" by Joe Coogan. Published in *Four Quarters Magazine*, January 1952. Reprinted by permission of the author.

DODD, MEAD & COMPANY. "Family Blessing" from *Nuts in May* by Cornelia Otis Skinner. Copyright 1948 by Cornelia Otis Skinner. Originally appeared in *The New Yorker*. Reprinted by permission of Dodd, Mead & Company.

DOUBLEDAY & COMPANY, INC. "When I Was Queen of the May," copyright © 1959 by Jean Kerr from the book *The Snake Has All the Lines* by Jean Kerr. Published in *Reader's Digest* as "Mom Were You Ever Miss Rheingold?" Reprinted by permission of William Heinemann Ltd. and Doubleday & Company, Inc.

"My Famous Grandfather," copyright © 1962 by Brian Friel. Appeared in *The Sign* as "Kelly's Hall," *The New Yorker*, and included in *The Saucer of Larks*. Reprinted by permission of Doubleday & Company, Inc.

"Dawn," copyright © 1956 by *Partisan Review*, from *The Presence of Grace* by J. F. Powers. First published in *Partisan Review*. Reprinted by permission of the author, A. M. Heath & Company, and Doubleday & Company, Inc.

FARRAR, STRAUS & CUDAHY, INC. "Mission Completed" from *What Is the Stars*, by Arthur J. Roth. Copyright © 1959 by Arthur J. Roth. Reprinted by permission of Farrar, Straus & Cudahy, Inc., and The Hutchinson Publishing Group.

"Hunger Strike" from *Don Camillo's Dilemma*, by Giovanni Guareschi. Copyright 1950 by Giovanni Guareschi.

"A Baptism" from *The Little World of Don Camillo*, by Giovanni Guareschi. Copyright 1954 by Giovanni Guareschi. Both reprinted by permission of Farrar, Straus & Cudahy, Inc.

HOUGHTON MIFFLIN COMPANY. "Their First Movie" from *The World, the Flesh, and Father Smith*, by Bruce Marshall. Copyright 1945 by Bruce Marshall. Reprinted by permission of Houghton Mifflin Company and A. Watkins, Inc.

ALFRED A. KNOPF, INC. "The First Confession" from *Stories of Frank O'Connor*. Copyright 1951, 1952 by Frank O'Connor. Reprinted by permission of Alfred A. Knopf, Inc., and Hamish Hamilton, Ltd.

"Taking the Veil" from *The Doves' Nest and Other Stories*, by Katherine Mansfield. Copyright 1923, 1937 by Alfred A. Knopf, Inc. Reprinted by permission of the publisher and The Society of Authors as the Literary Representative of the Estate of the late Miss Katherine Mansfield.

LITTLE, BROWN & COMPANY. Excerpts from "Knocko Minihan's Wake" from *The Last Hurrah*, by Edwin O'Connor. Copyright © 1956 by Edwin O'Connor. Reprinted by permission of Little, Brown & Company, The Atlantic Monthly Press, and A. D. Peters.

"Too, Too Sick-Making" from *Vile Bodies*, by Evelyn Waugh. Copyright 1930 by Evelyn Waugh. Reprinted by permission of Little, Brown & Company and Chapman and Hall Ltd.

THE MACMILLAN COMPANY. "My Vocation" from *Selected Stories*, by Mary Lavin. Copyright © 1956, 1959 by Mary Lavin. Reprinted by permission of The Macmillan Company.

NEW AMERICAN LIBRARY. "The Powers of Imagination" by Eric Cross. Appeared in *The Irish Genius*, edited by Devin Garrity. New American Library, New York.

THE NEW YORKER. "Mother Coakley's Reform" by Brendan Gill. Copyright © 1944, *The New Yorker Magazine, Inc.*

"Can't Slip Any Drugs to Sisters on Fifth Avenue" by John McNulty. Copyright © 1947, *The New Yorker Magazine, Inc.* Both reprinted by permission of *The New Yorker*.

ST. JOHN ERVINE. "The Burial" by St. John Ervine. Reprinted by permission of the author.

SHEED & WARD, INC. "Poor Bandaged Children of Eve" from *Shepherd's Tartan*, by Sister Mary Jean Dorcy, O.P. Copyright 1953 by Sheed & Ward, Inc.

"Jeanmaire, Jeanmaire!" from *The Mouse Hunter*, by Lucile Hasley. Copyright 1953 by Sheed & Ward, Inc. Both reprinted by permission of Sheed & Ward, Inc., New York, and Sheed & Ward Limited, London.

"The Extraordinary Cabman" from *Tremendous Trifles*, by G. K. Chesterton. Copyright 1909. Published by Sheed & Ward, Inc., New York. Reprinted by permission of Miss Dorothy Collins and the publishers.

SIMON & SCHUSTER, INC. "There's a Spot in My Heart" from *There's a Spot in My Heart*, by Frank Leslie. Copyright 1947 by Frank Leslie. Reprinted by permission of Simon & Schuster, Inc., and William Heinemann Ltd.

THE VIKING PRESS, INC. "The Confessional" from *A Purse of Coffers*, by Sean O'Faolain. Copyright 1938 by Sean O'Faolain. Reprinted by permission of The Viking Press, Inc., and Jonathan Cape Limited.

"The Temptations of Saint Anthony," "The Giveaway," "Simeon Stylites" from *Times Three*, by Phyllis McGinley. Copyright 1954 by Phyllis McGinley. Reprinted by permission of The Viking Press, Inc.

"Pipe Line and Sinker" from *The Province of the Heart*, by Phyllis McGinley. Copyright © 1958 by Phyllis McGinley. Reprinted by permission of The Viking Press, Inc., and The World's Work Ltd.

CONTENTS

INTRODUCTION

The past few years have not, by and large, been comfortable ones for American Catholics. They have been accused of stuffing ballot boxes, favoring fluoridation and criticizing Betty Crocker, to mention only a few of the more serious charges placed against members of that monolithic establishment, the Church of Rome, sometimes more affectionately known as "the Papist Plot." (We like to be in fashion, so we're striking an ecumenical note right here at the beginning.) For the most part, Catholics have learned to turn aside these well-meant little nosegays and proceed about their business. After all, what's a little throat slashing among friends?

But Catholics can be pushed too far, and the one charge that will bring them out fighting, rosaries flying, no holds barred, is that they lack a sense of humor. Their violent reaction proves, of course, that they are 100 per cent Americans—since all true Americans are fiercely proud of their self-claimed roles as the great humorists of the Western World.

And yet evidence that Catholics en masse are a fairly grim group is, we fear, too abundant to be denied, at least by us. We planned here to illustrate this thesis by presenting prime examples from our "Catholic Stuffed Shirt and Pompous Piety File"—true anecdotes collected at great personal risk in the trackless rain forests of parish socials, Holy Name Society meetings and Knights of Columbus outings. Some uncharitable souls might judge our decision not to do so as cowardice; we prefer to think of it as prudence.

This problem of humor and Catholics has always intrigued us, and we decided to find out for ourselves if circumstantial evidence proved only that we had been associating with the wrong kind of Catholics. Somewhere, we felt, beneath the dour and self-important topsoil there must lie a rich vein of true humor. We started to dig, and this book is the result.

We are convinced, of course, that we found gold in the form of the stories, poems, essays and sketches presented here. And we see this collection as a sort of challenge to American Catholics, and especially to Catholic book reviewers. If you critics don't think that this is a funny book, it proves what we have always suspected, that you are grouty, cross-grained churls. And readers, if you don't buy it in large quantities, you can write yourselves off as hopelessly devoid of all real warmth, wit and wisdom. Shame on you!

DAN HERR
JOEL WELLS

BLITHE SPIRITS

Sean O'Faolain

THE CONFESSIONAL

In the wide nave the wintry evening light was faint as gloom, and in the shadows of the aisle it was like early night. There was no sound in the chapel but the wind blowing up from the river valley, or an occasional tiny noise when a brass socket creaked under the great heat of a dying flame. To the three small boys crouched together on a bench in the farther aisle, holding each other's hands, listening timidly to the crying wind, staring wide-eyed at the candles, it seemed odd that in such a storm the bright flames never moved.

Suddenly the eldest of the three, a redheaded little ruffian, whispered loudly; but the other two, staring at the distant face of the statue, silenced him with a great hiss like a breaking wave. In another moment the lad in the center, crouching down in fear and gripping the hand on each side of him, whispered so quietly that they barely heard, "She's moving."

For a second or two they did not even breathe. Then all three expelled a deep sigh of disappointment.

It was Monday afternoon, and every Monday, as they had each heard tell over and over again in their homes, Father Hanafin spoke with the Blessed Virgin in the grotto. Some said she came late at night; some said in the early morning before the chapel was opened; some said it was the time when the sun goes down; but until now nobody had dared to watch. To be sure, Father Hanafin was not in the chapel now, but for all that, the three little spies had come filled with high hope. The eldest spoke their bitter disappointment aloud.

"It's all my eye," he said angrily. The other two felt that what he had said was true, but they pretended to be deeply shocked.

"That's an awful thing you said, Foxer," whispered the boy in the middle.

"Go away, you, Philpot!" said Foxer.

"Gor! I think it's a cause for confession, Foxer!" whispered Philpot again.

"It's a mortal sin, Foxer!" said the third, leaning over to say it.

"Don't you try to cod me, Cooney, or I'll burst yer jaw!" cried Foxer angrily.

Philpot hushed them sternly and swiftly, but the spell was broken. They all leaned back in the bench.

Beside them was Father Hanafin's confession box, its worn purple curtain partly drawn back, his worn purple stole hanging on a crook on the wall inside, and as Foxer gazed into the box with curiosity the Adversary tempted him in his heart.

"Come on, Cooney!" he invited at last. "Come on, and I'll hear yer confession."

"Gor! Come on," said Cooney, rising.

"That's a sin," said Philpot, though secretly eager to sit in the priest's chair.

"You're an awful ould Aunt Mary!" jeered Foxer, whereupon all Philpot's scruples vanished and the three scrambled for the confessor's seat. But Foxer was there before either of them, and at once he swished the curtains together as he had seen Father Hanafin do, and put the long stole about his neck. It was so nice in there in the dark that he forgot his two penitents waiting beyond the closed grilles on either side, and he was putting imaginary snuff into his nostrils and flicking imaginary specks of snuff from his chest when Cooney's angry face appeared between the curtains.

"Are yeh going to hear me confession, Foxer, or are yeh not?" he cried in a rage, eager for his turn to be priest.

"Go back, my child," said Foxer crossly, and he swished the curtains together again. Then, as if in spite, he leaned over to the opposite grille and slowly and solemnly he drew the slide and peered into the frightened eyes of Philpot.

"Tell me how long since your last confession, my child," he said gravely.

"Twenty years," whispered Philpot in awe.

"What have you done since then?" intoned Foxer sadly.

"I stole sweets, Father. And I forgot my prayers. And I cursed, Father."

"You cursed!" thundered Foxer. "What curse did you say?"

"I said that our master was an ould sod, Father," murmured Philpot timidly.

"So he is, my child. Is there anything else?"

"No, Father."

"For your penance say two hundred and forty-nine Rosaries, and four hundred and seventy Our Fathers, and three hundred and thirty-two Hail Marys. And now be a good, obedient boy. And pray for me, won't you? Gawd bless you, my child."

And with that Foxer drew the slide slowly before the small astonished face.

As he turned to the other side his hand fell on a little box—it was Father Hanafin's consolation during the long hours spent in that stuffy confessional listening to the sins and sorrows of his parishioners. Foxer's awkward fingers lifted the cover, and the sweet scent rose powerfully through the darkness as he coaxed the loose snuff down from the cover. Then drawing the slide on Cooney, he gravely inhaled a pinch and leaned his ear to the cool iron of the grille.

Outside a footstep sounded on the marble floor, and peering out Foxer saw the priest walk slowly up the farther aisle, turn and walk slowly down again, his breviary held high to the slanting radiance of the Virgin's altar.

"It's Father Hanafin," whispered Foxer to Cooney; and to Philpot, "Keep quiet or we're all ruined."

Up and down the solemn footsteps went, and high above their heads in the windows of the clerestory and along the lath and plaster of the rood the wind moaned and fingered the loose slates, and now and again they heard the priest murmur aloud the deep, open vowels of his prayer, "*Gaudeamus*

Domine," or "*Domine, Domine meo*," in a long, breathing sigh.

"He's talking to the Virgin," breathed Cooney to Foxer.

"He's talking to the Virgin," breathed Foxer in turn to Philpot.

"Amen," sighed the priest, and went on his knees before the candles that shone steadily and were reflected brilliantly in the burnished brass.

The three spies had begun to peep from their hiding place when the snuff fell on Foxer's lap and the grains began to titillate his nose. In agony he held his mouth for a full minute and then burst into a furious sneeze. In astonishment the priest gazed about him, and once again Foxer held his breath and once again he sneezed. At the third sneeze the priest gazed straight at the box.

"Come out!" he said in a loud voice. "Come out of that box!"

And as the three guilty forms crept from the three portals he commanded again, "Come here!"

Awkwardly they stumbled forward through the seats, trying to hide behind one another until they stood before him.

"What were you doing in there?" he asked Foxer.

"I was hearing their confessions, Father." Foxer trembled and half raised his arm as if to ward off a blow.

For a moment the priest glared at him and then he asked, "And what penance did you give?"

"I—I gave three hundred and thirty-two Hail Marys, Father, and I think it was four hundred Our Fathers, Father, and two hundred and forty-nine Rosaries, Father."

"Well!" pronounced the priest in a solemn voice. "Go home and let each one of ye say that penance three times over before nine o'clock tomorrow morning."

Stumbling over one another's heels, the three crept down the dark aisle and crushed out through the green baize door and into the falling night that was torn by the storm. The street lamps were lit, and under one of these they halted and looked at each other, angry and crestfallen.

"Nine hundred and ninety Hail Marys!" wailed Philpot, and Cooney squared up to Foxer with clenched fists.

"Yerrah!" said Foxer. "It's all a cod!"

And he raced suddenly away to his supper, followed by the shouts and feet of the other two.

J. F. Powers

DAWN

Father Udovic placed the envelope before the Bishop and stepped back. He gave the Bishop more than enough time to read what was written on the envelope, time to digest *The Pope* and, down in the corner, the *Personal*, and then he stepped forward. "It was in the collection yesterday," he said. "At Cathedral."

"Peter's Pence, Father?"

Father Udovic nodded. He'd checked that. It had been in with the special Peter's Pence envelopes, and not with the regular Sunday ones.

"Well, then . . ." The Bishop's right hand opened over the envelope, then stopped and came to roost again, uneasily, on the edge of the desk.

Father Udovic shifted a foot; popped a knuckle in his big toe. The envelope was a bad thing all right. They'd never received anything like it. The Bishop was doing what Father Udovic had done when confronted by the envelope, thinking twice, which was what Monsignor Renton at Cathedral had done, and his curates before him, and his housekeeper who counted the collection. In the end, each had seen the envelope as a hot potato and passed it on. But the Bishop couldn't do that. He didn't know *what* might be inside. Even Father Udovic, who had held it up to a strong light, didn't know. That was the hell of it.

The Bishop continued to stare at the envelope. He still hadn't touched it.

"It beats me," said Father Udovic, moving backward. He sank down on the leather sofa.

"Was there something else, Father?"

Father Udovic got up quickly and went out of the office—wondering how the Bishop would handle the problem, disappointed that he evidently meant to handle it by himself. In a way, Father Udovic felt responsible. It had been his idea to popularize the age-old collection—"to personalize Peter's Pence"—by moving the day for it ahead a month, so that the Bishop, who was going to Rome, would be able to present the proceeds to the Holy Father personally. There had been opposition from the very first. Monsignor Renton, the rector at Cathedral, and one of those at table when Father Udovic proposed his plan, was ill disposed to it (as he was to Father Udovic himself) and had almost killed it with his comment, "Smart promotion, Bruno." (Monsignor Renton's superior attitude was understandable. He'd had Father Udovic's job, that of chancellor of the diocese, years ago, under an earlier bishop.) But Father Udovic had won out. The Bishop had written a letter incorporating Father Udovic's idea. The plan had been poorly received in some rectories, which was to be expected since it disturbed the routine schedule of special collections. Father Udovic, however, had been confident that the people, properly appealed to, could do better than in the past with Peter's Pence. And the first returns, which had reached him that afternoon, were reassuring—whatever the envelope might be.

It was still on the Bishop's desk the next day, off to one side, and it was there on the day after. On the following day, Thursday, it was in the "In" section of his file basket. On Friday it was still there, buried. Obviously the Bishop was stumped.

On Saturday morning, however, it was back on the desk. Father Udovic, called in for consultation, had a feeling, a really satisfying feeling, that the Bishop might have need of him. If so, he would be ready. He had a plan. He sat down on the sofa.

"It's about this," the Bishop said, glancing down at the envelope before him. "I wonder if you can locate the sender."

"I'll do my best," said Father Udovic. He paused to consider whether it would be better just to go and do his best, or to present his plan of operation to the Bishop for approval. But the Bishop, not turning to him at all, was outlining what he wanted done. And it was Father Udovic's own plan! The Cathedral priests at their Sunday Masses should request the sender of the envelope to report to the sacristy afterward. The sender should be assured that the contents would be turned over to the Holy Father, if possible.

"Providing, of course," said Father Udovic, standing and trying to get into the act, "it's not something—"

"Providing it's possible to do so."

Father Udovic tried not to look sad. The Bishop might express himself better, but he was saying nothing that hadn't occurred to Father Udovic first, days before. It was pretty discouraging.

He retreated to the outer office and went to work on a memo of their conversation. Drafting letters and announcements was the hardest part of his job for him. He tended to go astray without a memo, to take up with the tempting clichés that came to him in the act of composition and sometimes perverted the Bishop's true meaning. Later that morning he called Monsignor Renton and read him the product of many revisions, the two sentences.

"Okay," said Monsignor Renton. "I'll stick it in the bulletin. Thanks a lot."

As soon as Father Udovic hung up, he doubted that that was what the Bishop wished. He consulted the memo. The Bishop was very anxious that "not too much be made of this matter." Naturally Monsignor Renton wanted the item for his parish bulletin. He was hard up. At one time he had produced the best bulletin in the diocese, but now he was written out, quoting more and more from the magazines and even from the papal encyclicals. Father Udovic called Monsignor Renton back and asked that the announcement be kept out of print. It would be enough to read it once over lightly from the pulpit, using Father Udovic's version, because it said enough without saying too much and was, he implied, authorized by the Bishop. Whoever the announcement concerned would comprehend it. If published, the announcement would be subject to study and private interpretation. "Announcements from the pulpit are soon forgotten," Father Udovic said. "I mean—by the people they don't concern."

"You were right the first time, Bruno," said Monsignor Renton. He sounded sore.

The next day—Sunday—Father Udovic stayed home, expecting a call from Monsignor Renton, or possibly even a visit. There was nothing. That evening he called the Cathedral rectory and got one of the curates. Monsignor Renton wasn't expected in until very late. The curate had made the announcement at his two Masses, but no one had come to him about it. "Yes, Father, as you say, it's quite possible someone came to Monsignor about it. Probably he didn't consider it important enough to call you about."

"*Not important!*"

"Not important enough to call *you* about, Father. On *Sunday*."

"I see," said Father Udovic mildly. It was good to know that the curate, after almost a year of listening to Monsignor Renton, was still respectful. Some of the men out in parishes said Father Udovic's job was a snap, and maintained that he'd landed it only because he employed the touch system of typing. Before hanging up, Father Udovic stressed the importance of resolving the question of the envelope, but somehow (words played tricks on him) he sounded as though he were accusing the curate of indifference. What a change! The curate didn't take criticism very well, as became all too clear from his sullen silence, and he wasn't very loyal. When Father Udovic suggested that Monsignor Renton might have neglected to make the announcement at his Masses, the curate readily agreed. "Could've slipped his mind all right. I guess you know what that's like."

Early the next morning Father Udovic was in touch with Monsignor Renton, beginning significantly with a glowing report on the Peter's Pence collection, but the conversation languished, and finally he had to ask about the announcement.

"Nobody showed," Monsignor Renton said in an annoyed voice. "What d'ya want to do about it?"

"Nothing right now," said Father Udovic, and hung up. If there had been a failure in the line of communication, he thought he knew where it was.

The envelope had reposed on the Bishop's desk over the weekend and through most of Monday. But that afternoon Father Udovic, on one of his appearances in the Bishop's office, noticed that it was gone. As soon as the Bishop left for the day, Father Udovic rushed in, looking first in the wastebasket, then among the sealed outgoing letters, for a moment actually expecting to see a fat one addressed in the Bishop's hand to the Apostolic Delegate. When he uncovered the envelope in the "Out" section of the file basket, he wondered at himself for looking in the other places first. The envelope had to be filed somewhere—a separate folder would be best—but Father Udovic didn't file it. He carried it to his desk. There, sitting down to it in the gloom of the outer office, weighing, feeling, smelling the envelope, he succumbed entirely to his first fears. He remembered the parable of the cockle. "An enemy hath done this." An enemy was plotting to disturb the peace of the diocese, to employ the Bishop as an agent against himself or against some other innocent person, some unsuspecting priest or nun—yes, against Father Udovic. Why him? Why not? Only a diseased mind would contemplate such a scheme, Father Udovic thought, but that didn't make it less likely. And the sender, whoever he was, doubtless anonymous and judging others by himself, would assume that the envelope had already been opened and that the announcement was calculated to catch him. Such a person would never come forward.

Father Udovic's fingers tightened on the envelope. He could rip it open, but he wouldn't. That evening, enjoying instant coffee in his room, he could steam it open. But he wouldn't. In the beginning, the envelope might have been opened. It would have been so easy, pardonable then. Monsignor Renton's housekeeper might have done it. With the Bishop honoring the name on the envelope and the intentions of whoever wrote it, up to a point, anyway, there was now a principle operating that just couldn't be bucked. Monsignor Renton could have it his way.

That evening Father Udovic called him and asked that the announcement appear in the bulletin.

"Okay. I'll stick it in. It wouldn't surprise me if we got some action now."

"I hope so," said Father Udovic, utterly convinced that Monsignor Renton had failed him before. "Do you mind taking it down verbatim this time?"

"Not at all."

In the next bulletin, an advance copy of which came to Father Udovic through the courtesy of Monsignor Renton, the announcement appeared in an expanded, unauthorized version.

The result on Sunday was no different.

During the following week Father Udovic considered the possibility that the sender was a floater, and thought of having the announcement broadcast from every pulpit in the diocese. He would need the Bishop's permission for that, though, and he didn't dare to ask for something he probably wouldn't get. The Bishop had instructed him not to make too much of the matter. The sender would have to be found at Cathedral or not at all. If not at all, Father Udovic, having done his best, would understand that he wasn't supposed to know any more about the envelope than he did. He would file it away, and some other chancellor, some other bishop, perhaps, would inherit it. The envelope was most likely harmless, anyway, but Father Udovic wasn't so much relieved as bored by the probability that some poor soul was trusting the Bishop to put the envelope into the hands of the Holy Father, hoping for rosary beads blessed by him or for his autographed picture, and enclosing a small offering, perhaps a spiritual bouquet. Toward the end of the week Father Udovic told the Bishop that he liked to think that the envelope contained a spiritual bouquet from a little child, and that its contents had already been delivered, so to speak; its prayers and communions already credited to the Holy Father's account in heaven.

"I must say I hadn't thought of that," said the Bishop.

Unfortunately for his peace of mind, Father Udovic wasn't always able to believe that the sender was a little child.

The most persistent of those coming to him in reverie was a middle-aged woman saying she hadn't received a special Peter's Pence envelope, had been out of town a few weeks, and so hadn't heard or read the announcement. When Father Udovic tried her on the meaning of the *Personal* on the envelope, however, the woman just went away; and so did all the other suspects under questioning—except one. This was a rich old man suffering from scrupulosity. He wanted his alms to be in secret, as it said in Scripture, lest he be deprived of his eternal reward; but not entirely in secret. That was as far as Father Udovic could figure the old man. Who was he? An audacious old Protestant who hated communism; or could some future Knight of St. Gregory be taking his first awkward step? The old man was pretty hard to believe in, and the handwriting on the envelope sometimes struck Father Udovic as that of a woman. This wasn't necessarily bad. Women controlled the nation's wealth. He'd seen the figures on it. The explanation was simple: widows. Perhaps they hadn't taken the right tone in the announcement. Father Udovic's version had been safe and cold; Monsignor Renton's like a summons. It might have been emphasized that the Bishop, under certain circumstances, would *gladly* undertake to deliver the envelope. That might have made a difference. The sender would not only have to appreciate the difficulty of the Bishop's position, but abandon his own. That wouldn't be easy for the sort of person Father Udovic had in mind. He had a feeling that it wasn't going to happen. The Bishop would leave for Rome on the following Tuesday. So time was running out. The envelope could contain a check—quite the cruelest thought—on which payment would be stopped after a limited time by the donor, whom Father Udovic persistently saw as an old person not to be dictated to; or it could be nullified even sooner by untimely death. God, what a shame! In Rome, where the needs of the world, temporal as well as spiritual, were so well known, the Bishop would've been welcome as the flowers in May.

And then, having come full circle, Father Udovic would be hard on himself for dreaming and see the envelope as a whited sepulcher concealing all manner of filth, spelled out in letters snipped from newsprint, and calculated to shake Rome's faith in him. It was then that he particularly liked to think of the sender as a little child. But soon the middle-aged woman would be back, and all the others, among whom the hottest suspect was a feeble-minded nun—devils all to pester him, and the last was always worse than the first. For he always ended up with the old man—and what if there was such an old man?

On Saturday, Father Udovic called Monsignor Renton and asked him to run the announcement again. It was all they could do, he said, and admitted that he had little hope of success.

"Don't let it throw you, Bruno. It's always darkest before dawn."

Father Udovic said he no longer cared. He said he liked to think that the envelope contained a spiritual bouquet from a little child, that its contents had already been delivered, its prayers and communions already. . . .

"You should've been a nun, Bruno."

"Not sure I know what you mean," Father Udovic said, and hung up. He wished it were in his power to do something about Monsignor Renton. Some of the old ones got funny when they stayed too long in one place.

On Sunday, after the eight o'clock Mass, Father Udovic received a call from Monsignor Renton. "I told 'em if somebody didn't own up to the envelope, we'd open it. I guess I got carried away." But it had worked. Monsignor Renton had just talked with the party responsible for the envelope—

a Mrs. Anton—and she was on the way over to see Father
Udovic.

"A woman, huh?"

"A widow. That's about all I know about her."

"A widow, huh? Did she say what was in it?"

"I'm afraid it's not what you thought, Bruno. It's money."

Father Udovic returned to the front parlor, where he had
left Mrs. Anton. "The Bishop'll see you," he said, and sat
down. She wasn't making a good impression on him. She
could've used a shave. When she'd asked for the Bishop, Father Udovic had replied instinctively, "He's busy," but it
hadn't convinced her. She had appeared quite capable of walking out on him. He invoked the Bishop's name again. "Now,
one of the things the Bishop'll want to know is why you didn't
show up before this."

Mrs. Anton gazed at him, then past him, as she had when
he'd tried to question her. He saw her starting to get up, and
thought he was about to lose her. He hadn't heard the Bishop
enter the room.

The Bishop waved Mrs. Anton down, seated himself near
the doorway at some distance from them, and motioned Father
Udovic to continue.

To the Bishop it might sound like browbeating, but Father
Udovic meant to go on being firm with Mrs. Anton. He hadn't
forgotten that she'd responded to Monsignor Renton's threats.
"Why'd you wait so long? You listen to the Sunday announcements, don't you?" If she persisted in ignoring him, she could
make him look bad, of course, but he didn't look for her to
do that, with the Bishop present.

Calmly Mrs. Anton spoke, but not to Father Udovic.
"Call off your trip?"

The Bishop shook his head.

In Father Udovic's opinion, it was one of his functions to
protect the Bishop from directness of that sort. "How do we
know what's in here?" he demanded. Here, unfortunately, he
reached up the wrong sleeve of his cassock for the envelope.

Then he had it. "What's in here? Money?" He knew from Monsignor Renton that the envelope contained money, but he hadn't told the Bishop, and so it probably sounded rash to him. Father Udovic could feel the Bishop disapproving of him; and Mrs. Anton still hadn't answered the question.

"Maybe you should return the envelope to Mrs. Anton, Father," said the Bishop.

That did it for Mrs. Anton. "It's got a dollar in it," she said.

Father Udovic glanced at the Bishop. The Bishop was adjusting his cuffs. This was something he did at funerals and public gatherings. It meant that things had gone on too long. Father Udovic's fingers were sticking to the envelope. He still couldn't believe it. "Feels like there's more than that," he said.

"I wrapped it up good in paper."

"You didn't write a letter or anything?"

"Was I supposed to?"

Father Udovic came down on her. "You were supposed to do what everybody else did. You were supposed to use the envelopes we had printed up for the purpose." He went back a few steps in his mind. "You told Monsignor Renton what was in the envelope?"

"Yes."

"Did you tell him how much?"

"No."

"Why not?"

"*He* didn't ask me."

And *he* didn't have to, thought Father Udovic. One look at Mrs. Anton and Monsignor Renton would know. Parish priests got to know such things. They were like weight-guessers, for whom it was only a question of ounces. Monsignor Renton shouldn't have passed Mrs. Anton on. He had opposed the plan to personalize Peter's Pence, but who would have thought he'd go to such lengths to get even with Father Udovic? It was sabotage. Father Udovic held out the envelope and pointed to the *Personal* on it. "What do you mean by that?" Here was where the creatures of his dreams had always gone away. He leaned forward for the answer.

Mrs. Anton leaned forward to give it. "I mean I don't want somebody else takin' all the credit with the Holy Father!"

Father Udovic sank back. It had been bad before, when she'd ignored him, but now it was worse. She was attacking the Bishop. If there were only a way to *prove* she was out of her mind; if only she'd say something that would make all her remarks acceptable in retrospect. . . . "How's the Holy Father gonna know who this dollar came from if you didn't write anything?"

"I wrote my name and address on it. In ink."

"All right, Father," said the Bishop. He stood up and almost went out of the room before he stopped and looked back at Mrs. Anton. "Why don't you send it by regular mail?"

"He'd never see it! That's why! Some flunky'd get hold of it! Same as here! Oh, don't I know!"

The Bishop walked out, leaving them together—with the envelope.

In the next few moments, although Father Udovic knew he had an obligation to instruct Mrs. Anton, and had the text for it—"When thou doest an almsdeed, sound not a trumpet before thee"—he despaired. He realized that they had needed each other to arrive at their sorry state. It seemed to him, sitting there saying nothing, that they saw each other as two people who'd sinned together on earth might see each other in hell, unchastened even then, only blaming each other for what had happened.

Edwin O'Connor

KNOCKO MINIHAN'S WAKE

At 7:30, Adam was waiting; Skeffington, on the other hand, was not. His unpunctuality inviolable, he was fifteen minutes late, and as the long official car pulled up he said genially, "Hop in. As a taxpayer, you're entitled to. Try the comforts of the vehicle you so thoughtfully provided for me."

Adam got in. Determined to remove all mystery from the outset, he said, "By the way, when we were talking this afternoon I completely forgot to ask you where we were going."

"So you did," Skeffington said. "I took it as a rare mark of confidence; now I find it was only a lapse of memory. One more illusion lost." He chuckled and said, "Actually, we're going to a wake. Knocko Minihan's wake."

"A *wake?*"

"Surprised? I had an idea you might be: there was just the possibility that you weren't in the habit of spending your free evenings in visiting deceased strangers. But I felt that tonight it might be useful for you to come along. In its way, a wake can be quite an occasion."

"You may be underestimating me," Adam said. "I've been to a few wakes. Not many, but a few."

"I don't doubt it. Probably not exactly like this one, however. Not that poor Knocko's will be unique, but it might be a little different from those you've been to."

Adam was not prepared to dispute this. The car drove on, and he said, "His name wasn't Knocko, surely?"

"No. It was Aram. The mother was part French, and he was named for an uncle in Quebec. The old gentleman had some money, and the Minihans cherished the fond hope that one happy day it would fall into the lap of little Aram. Unfortunately there was a tragic development. The uncle went crazy and gave away all his money to a convent outside Montreal; two months later he went to a Canadian lunatic asylum where he subsequently died. The Minihans naturally tried to prove that he'd been a madman before he gave the money to the convent. It seemed a reasonable assumption, especially when you consider that the old man suffered from the delusion that he was an air rifle, and went around spitting BB's at squirrels. But as anybody can tell you who's ever tried to recover a bequest from an order of nuns in Quebec, the assumption wasn't quite reasonable enough. So no legacy was forthcoming for the little Aram. Meanwhile, of course, he'd been stuck with the name: I don't think he ever forgave his parents for that. It was a terrible start in life for a boy in this city. That's why he gladly became Knocko."

"And how did he make out after this terrible start?"

"Not too well. Save in one respect, that is. He married a grand woman who was a close friend of my wife's—your aunt's," he said. "In every other way he was a failure. He had a hardware store that he ran into the ground almost before the opening-day sale was over. Then he tried several other businesses, all of which petered out in no time at all. I don't know that people trusted him especially, and they certainly didn't like him. And neither," he said, rather surprisingly, "did I. However, *de mortuis* . . ."

"If nobody liked him," Adam said, "I imagine we'll run into a fairly slim attendance tonight."

"Not at all," said Skeffington. "The place'll be crowded to the doors. A wake isn't quite the same as a popularity contest. There are other factors involved. Ah, here we are."

They had arrived in front of a two-story frame tenement house which was in need of paint; the door on the left held a wreath with a large purple ribbon. Skeffington placed a hand just beneath this ornament and then, before pushing the door open, paused to regard the unlovely premises. He shook his head. "Charming," he said. "Come on, let's go in."

A heavy-set woman, dressed in black, and with the face of

some large and extremely suspicious bird, came out of the darkness to greet them.

"Hello, Frank," she said.

"Hello, Agnes. Mrs. Burns, my nephew, Adam Caulfield. Mary's boy." There were nods, an exchange of greetings; Skeffington asked, "How's Gert taking it?"

"Pretty good. She cries a little," said the woman. Adam could not help but observe that she was herself noticeably dry of eye. In explanation she added, "She remembers all the nice things he done."

"She has a remarkable memory," Skeffington said dryly.

Mrs. Burns accepted this with a short nod of agreement, then pointed to a door on the right of the narrow hall. "He's in the parlor," she said. "I think there's no one in there now; it's still a bit early. Go right in, Frank. He looks lovely."

Adam followed Skeffington into the parlor: he saw a tall, glum room which might have been designed specifically with this melancholy event in mind. Heavy dull plush furniture had been pushed back against the walls; stretching from side to side across the room were rows of thin metal chairs of the kind furnished by catering services. At the moment these were empty; looking at them through the gloom, Adam wondered whether this was indeed due to the hour of their arrival, or rather to the simple fact that Knocko Minihan had not been widely loved.

At the far end of the parlor, decorated with wreaths and floral sprays, was a gray coffin; to Adam it seemed huge, a sarcophagus fit for a giant. He advanced upon it with his uncle; they knelt by the side of the coffin, and Adam saw Knocko in death. He lay stiffly among billows of white satin, a diminutive man lost in the recesses of his mighty container. Across the top of his head occasional strands of yellowish-white hair had been combed strategically; a taut, grudging smile, which somehow fell short of suggesting an interior peace, had been worked into position. His small hands were folded across his chest, clasping a rosary, and over the coffin a large crucifix, heavily studded with rhinestones, had been suspended. Someone of ingenious mind—undoubtedly the undertaker, thought Adam—had fixed a baby spotlight so that it played full upon the crucifix; high above Knocko's final, alien smile, the rhinestones glittered and danced.

Adam said a prayer for this man he had not known. Skeffington, after a moment, got to his feet slowly, looking about him, at the coffin, at the crucifix. "A lavish display," he said. "And you couldn't get the man near a theater in his life." He put his hand lightly on Adam's shoulder and said, "Will you do me a favor and stay here a moment? I have to go in and say a word to the widow."

Adam looked up, surprised; he rose quickly. "You mean, wait *here?*"

Skeffington smiled slightly. "I'm afraid I do; it seems to be about the only place. You could wait in the car, but I've sent the chauffeur on an errand. In any event, it won't be too bad; I'll be back directly. Why don't you just sit down in one of those chairs in back? People will be coming in shortly, and, anyway, the whole thing is an experience you ought to have; it's a custom that's dying out. Besides, you can regard it as a meritorious act; you'll be keeping poor Knocko company."

Adam nodded reluctantly. There seemed nothing to do but agree, although he was scarcely happy over the prospect of the solitary vigil. Feeling vaguely that he had once again been outgeneraled all along the line, he moved toward the back of the room, as far as possible from the dead Knocko, the rhinestones, and the baby spotlight. Here in the dim light of the evening he sat down to await the return of his uncle.

In the first few minutes of his wait, the quiet, as well as the gloom, became increasingly uninviting. All light from the outside seemed to fade; the macabre cruciform dazzle above the coffin dominated the room. From somewhere there came the sound of a banging door; no one entered. Adam had indeed, as he had said earlier to Skeffington, attended a few wakes, but his memory of them was obscure. Now in this silent gloom he had a disquieting recollection of a story of Synge's about a wake in the Aran Islands: the long procession of shawled and sobbing women gathering at the bier, rocking back and forth to the wail of the keen. That such a scene could be duplicated in the parlor of Knocko Minihan tonight was wildly improbable; nevertheless, Adam found himself speculating upon it in some detail. Suddenly, from somewhere to his right there came a sound. "*Sssst!*" it hissed.

He jumped, startled. He turned and at first saw no one; then, in a corner which was darker than the rest of the room because of the shadow of a partially opened door, he saw a small, puckered woman, peering out at him with lively eyes.

"Did I *scare* you?" she asked. The possibility seemed to delight her.

"No," Adam lied stoutly. "You startled me. I didn't see you come in."

"Ah, I *was* in," she said. "I was here in my corner when you come in with Frank. Are you the nephew?"

Adam nodded. It seemed to him that with the discovery of this silent little watcher of the shadows a new dimension of eeriness had entered the room. She had spoken of "*my* corner" with a proud possessiveness, almost as if she had come in with the coffin and would remain in her appointed place, firm, open eyed, and irremovable, until it was taken away.

"I'm Delia Boylan," she said. "I knew your pa and I knew your ma and I knew you when you was a baby." Pepper-and-salt eyebrows rose as she considered him now. "You was homely as spit," she said.

"Ah," said Adam. How did one respond more fully to such frankness? He had no idea. He said, changing the subject hopefully, "I'm surprised there are so few people here to see Mr. Minihan."

"Ah, they'll be in," she said confidently. "They'll all want to get a good last look at old Knocko. There's them that's been waiting for it a long time. We're early. I always like to be a bit early." She raised herself to a half-standing posture and gazed critically at the coffin. "He looks grand with the cheeks all puffed out, don't he?" she asked.

She spoke of the corpse with the nonchalant detachment

possible only to those who have had vast experience with death. "He looks very nice," Adam said. He was painfully aware of his own lack of the special vocabulary of compliment appropriate to just such an occasion; he was sure that one existed. "Of course," he added, "I didn't know him when he was alive."

This, too, was maladroit; but Mrs. Boylan did not appear to mind. Her narrow little shoulders shrugged in contempt and she said, "A little runt of a man. Thin as a snake and no color to him at all. He was part French, you know."

"I know."

"That makes all the difference," she said mysteriously. "*Aram*. Ah, well, that's small matter now." She spoke as one forgiving him the injury of his ancestry. "God be good to the man," she said. "He was mean as a panther, but good luck to him."

Adam said nothing. Once more, there seemed to be nothing to say. The silence was broken by the entrance of a trio of mourners who came in, looked slowly about the room, nodded to Delia, then filed up to the coffin.

"The Carmichael girls," Delia explained, "with the brother Tim. *They* come early, as a general rule." She moved abruptly in her chair, stretching out to face the door. "*Ssst!*" she hissed.

Adam followed her glance. He saw a stout, balding young man, spruce and smooth in the discreet clothing of his profession, moving with purposeful yet superlatively respectful steps toward the coffin.

"*Ssst!*" Delia said again. "Johnnie!"

The young man paused and looked in their direction; Adam thought he appeared to be annoyed. In response to Delia's frantically beckoning hand he came over to them with an obvious reluctance.

"Johnnie Degnan," Delia said to Adam, adding unnecessarily, "the undertaker. We always like to have our little talk."

"Good evening, Mrs. Boylan," the undertaker said unenthusiastically.

"Ah, Johnnie," Delia said. She introduced Adam. "Frank Skeffington's nephew, Johnnie. The sister's boy."

The undertaker brightened; he made a short, formal bow. "Very pleased to meet you, sir," he said. "I've always been a great admirer of your uncle, although I've never had the pleasure of making his acquaintance. I hope that will be remedied tonight. Ah . . . was there anything in particular, Mrs. Boylan?"

"He looks grand, Johnnie," she said, waving toward the coffin. "Just grand. Did he take a lot of doing?"

An expression of slight strain appeared on the undertaker's round face; clearly, thought Adam, questions from the laity were not encouraged. "Mr. Minihan was in remarkable condition, Mrs. Boylan, for one of his advanced years," he said. He spoke in a low voice and with extraordinary rapidity, as if in the hope that by a sudden sprint through his words he might bring this interview to a close. It was a forlorn hope; Delia had reached out and grabbed the sleeve of his coat.

"And Johnnie," she said, "you laid him out in the *big* coffin! Ah, you rascal, you!" She rolled her eyes and released a little whoop of laughter; down by the coffin the Carmichael triumvirate turned in unison to stare. The undertaker made a swift, imploring pass with his hands, and Delia lowered her voice to a stage whisper. "My God," she said delightedly, "wouldn't it kill the man if he knew!"

The undertaker gave her a look of pain. "Mr. Minihan has a very fine casket," he said, emphasizing the final word. "As I'm sure he would have wished it."

"Ah," Delia said, "but the cost of it all! The cost, Johnnie!"

"Mr. Minihan," said the undertaker swiftly, "was a very prominent figure in the community. Very prominent."

Delia nodded agreeably. "He was the cheapest old devil that ever lived," she said. "And you know it. Well, he's gone now, poor man, and you done an elegant job on him, Johnnie." As a grace note she added, "No matter what you charge."

"Ah-ha-ha-ha," said the undertaker tonelessly, giving Adam a nervous smile, presumably meant to imply that they both were familiar with the irrepressible Mrs. Boylan. "Well, I must go now, Mrs. Boylan. Many duties. A pleasure to have met you sir. I hope to meet your uncle." He bowed again and hurried away on muted feet.

"There's a great rogue," Delia said approvingly. "Only thirty years old and he'd steal the skin off your bones. Just give him the chance and it's the big coffin, ten limousines, and the Holy Name Choir to sing you good-by."

"And is he responsible for the crucifix?" Adam asked, pointing to the dazzling object above the coffin.

"The pride and joy," she assured him. "It all goes on the bill." She shook with a sudden, rusty flutter of reminiscent mirth. "I says to him one day, I says, 'Don't you dare to stick that big sparkler over me when I'm gone, Johnnie Degnan! Don't you dare!' And he damn well won't; he knows he won't get a ten-cent piece out of me. Ah, he's the sly one," she said, "but he knows I'm on to him. *Sssst!*"

The sound, while no longer unfamiliar, was unexpected; Adam jumped again. An angular woman of forbidding aspect had come into the room and was now engaged in making hand signals to Delia.

"Aggie Gormley," Delia said. "I wonder has she news about the will? I'd best go see. I'll be back in a minute."

She hustled away with jerky, efficient steps, and Adam was alone once more.

He looked at Delia conversing with her newsy friend; he looked at the Carmichaels talking quietly to Johnnie Degnan; he looked at the coffin and the jewelry above it. He looked, too, at his watch and wondered absently when his uncle would return. Rather to his surprise, he did not greatly care, for he discovered to his horror that here in this presepulchral room reserved for mourning, and in the appalling company of Delia Boylan, he was undoubtedly enjoying himself.

. . . They went in, they knelt, and the Monsignor led them in the Rosary. They recited in unison the five decades of the beads which commemorate the Sorrowful Mysteries of the

Church; they prayed for the immortal soul of Aram Minihan. And as they prayed, their responses low, rhythmic, and at times not quite distinct, riding high over all other voices came one which to Adam was familiar, clear, unhesitating, and infinitely fervent. It was the voice of Delia Boylan.

The Rosary over, it was time to go. Skeffington swiftly and efficiently made the rounds, saying the necessary good-bys; then he signaled to Adam, and uncle and nephew walked toward the front door together. They had almost reached the door when Skeffington, suddenly halting, said, "Hold on a minute. I want a word with that undertaker before we go."

They both turned and saw the head of Johnnie Degnan poking out of the kitchen at the far end of the hall; obviously he had been watching their departure. Skeffington beckoned, and he came running quietly to them.

"Ah, good evening, Governor," he said, in his swift hushed tones. "A very sad occasion. I wanted to see you before this evening to make your acquaintance, but the pressure of my duties didn't quite allow. I'm John Degnan, Governor."

"Glad to know you, Mr. Degnan," Skeffington said. "As you say, it's a sad occasion. I'm happy to see you've done your best by it, however. I've been admiring your handiwork with the deceased."

"Thank you, Governor. Thank you very much. That's nice to hear. I did my best," the undertaker said modestly. "I don't mind telling you, Governor, that Mr. Minihan presented a very difficult case. Because of the age and the sunken cheeks and the wrinkles. I'm sure you can appreciate the difficulty of the task, Governor. Everything had to be smoothed out delicately, the youthful contours restored, and so forth."

"Yes. Now Mr. Degnan, only one feature of your work disturbs me, and that is the probable cost. You don't mind if I say that I was rather struck by the fact that the coffin, and what might be called the general death-room décor, seem a trifle splendid for someone who was in decidedly modest circumstances?"

The undertaker smiled; it was, Adam thought, a nervous

smile. "I see what you mean, Governor," he said swiftly. "I appreciate that point of view. And yet I always think the family is more satisfied if the final homage, as I like to think of it, is really nice in its every aspect. Something that the deceased would have been proud of if he could have seen it."

"Why, those are the feelings of an artist," Skeffington said. "They do you credit, Mr. Degnan. I presume, incidentally, that you've discussed all this with Mrs. Minihan?"

"Well, no. Not exactly, that is, Governor. I thought it best not to in her distraught condition. Just a few words here and there. I think you could say, more or less, that it was left to my discretion, as it so often is. I always believe in taking as many worries as possible from the shoulders of the family."

"That's very thoughtful of you. Now then, you're a young man, Mr. Degnan, but I understand you've had quite a bit of professional experience. As you might put it, you've been in charge of a good many final homages. Or as I might put it, you've buried a good many people. What would you say was the lowest price you've ever buried anyone for?"

"The lowest *price*, Governor?" The smile remained; it wavered uncertainly. "I don't quite understand. . . . What I mean to say is, Governor, I don't believe that's anything I've ever quite figured out."

"Try," Skeffington urged him. "Make a rough estimate. Would it be . . . oh, say thirty-five dollars?"

"*Thirty-five dollars!*" The gasp of astonishment and pain broke through the modulated occupational tones. The undertaker looked wildly at Skeffington and said, "You couldn't *begin* to bury anyone for that price today, Governor!"

"I'll bet you could if you really tried," Skeffington said pleasantly. "I'll bet you could both begin and end. And just to prove my confidence in your resourcefulness, Mr. Degnan, why don't you do that very thing with Mr. Minihan? Let's give it a real try. I think you can do it. I'm sure the final bill won't read over thirty-five dollars. Matter of fact, I'll instruct the widow to that effect immediately."

"But Governor, you can't be serious!" Degnan cried. The

smooth round face had become agonized; the soft hands were
united in front of him in a tight, beseeching clasp. He looked
as if he were about to hurl himself at his persecutor's feet, and
Adam, who had not until a moment ago realized just what it
was that his uncle was doing, now felt a sudden pity as well
as disgust for this abject little profiteer. "The costs alone, Governor," Degnan moaned. "They're going up every day. I
couldn't possibly do it. It's all *arranged*—"

"Fine," Skeffington said. "Then let it go through as arranged. But for thirty-five dollars."

"But, *Governor* . . ."

Skeffington pulled his watch from a vest pocket and examined it with apparent surprise. "It's later than I thought,"
he said. "Well, then, Mr. Degnan, it's all settled. I'll leave the
details to you. A suitable funeral conducted for thirty-five dollars, with no cutting of corners. All the normal courtesies extended; the usual paraphernalia available. I'll have a few men
on hand just to see that everything goes along well. I know
you'll do a grand job. In any event, I'll be sure to hear about it:
my observers will give me a full report."

The undertaker's face, which for some moments had been
the color of putty, had now turned a vivid red. "But Governor!
I hope you know how eager I am to co-operate in anything you
suggest. How eager I *always* am. But what you're asking is
impossible. . . ."

"Why, that's one of the words that doesn't belong to the
bright lexicon of youth," Skeffington said reprovingly. "I've
always believed that nothing is impossible when one has youth
and ambition. I hope you won't be the one to shake this treas-
ured belief. Because if you do," he said, regarding Degnan with
a stare which its recipient suddenly found as unpleasant as
anything he had ever experienced, "you might shake my confidence in you. What's worse, you might even begin to shake
public confidence in you. That is a bad thing to have happen
to a young undertaker with dreams, Mr. Degnan. You never
can tell how far it might reach. It might even reach the members of the licensing board for your profession. You never

know. But we mustn't keep you from your labors any longer. I suppose you have many things to do at a time like this. Possibly even more than you'd anticipated. Good night, Mr. Degnan. Glad you introduced yourself."

They went out the door and down the steps; Degnan's anguished voice trailed after them to their car. "Thirty-five dollars!" it wailed. "Governor, I *appeal* to you. . . ."

When they were under way, Skeffington said: "I hadn't planned on rounding your evening off in just that way. I hope you weren't too shocked by my treatment of the widow's helper."

Adam shook his head. "It seemed to me that the widow's helper rather had it coming. And will he do it for thirty-five dollars, do you think?"

Skeffington chuckled. "I wouldn't be surprised," he said dryly.

Phyllis McGinley

THREE POEMS

THE TEMPTATIONS OF
SAINT ANTHONY

Off in the wilderness bare and level,
Anthony wrestled with the Devil.
Once he'd beaten the Devil down,
Anthony'd turn his eyes toward town
And leave his hermitage now and then
To come to grips with the souls of men.

Afterward, all the tales agree,
Wrestling the Devil seemed to be
Quite a relief to Anthony.

THE GIVEAWAY

Saint Bridget was
A problem child.
Although a lass
Demure and mild,
And one who strove
To please her dad,
Saint Bridget drove
The family mad.
For here's the fault in Bridget lay:
She *would* give everything away.

To any soul
Whose luck was out

She'd give her bowl
Of stirabout;
She'd give her shawl,
Divide her purse
With one or all.
And what was worse,
When she ran out of things to give
She'd borrow from a relative.

Her father's gold,
Her grandsire's dinner,
She'd hand to cold
And hungry sinner;
Give wine, give meat,
No matter whose;
Take from her feet
The very shoes,
And when her shoes had gone to others,
Fetch forth her sister's and her mother's.

She could not quit.
She had to share;
Gave bit by bit
The silverware,
The barnyard geese,
The parlor rug,
Her little niece-
'S christening mug,
Even her bed to those in want,
And then the mattress of her aunt.

An easy touch
For poor and lowly,
She gave so much
And grew so holy
That when she died
Of years and fame,
The countryside

Put on her name,
And still the Isles of Erin fidget
With generous girls named Bride or Bridget.

Well, one must love her.
Nonetheless,
In thinking of her
Givingness,
There's no denial
She must have been
A sort of trial
To her kin.
The moral, too, seems rather quaint.
Who had the patience of a saint,
From evidence presented here?
Saint Bridget? Or her near and dear?

SIMEON STYLITES

On top of a pillar Simeon sat.
He wore no mantle,
He had no hat,
But bare as a bird
Sat night and day.
And hardly a word
Did Simeon say.

Under the sun of the desert sky
He sat on a pillar
Nine feet high.
When Fool and his brother
Came round to admire,
He raised it another
Nine feet high'r.

The seasons circled about his head.
He lived on water

And crusts of bread
(Or so one hears)
From pilgrim's store,
For thirty years
And a little more.

And why did Simeon sit like that,
Without a garment,
Without a hat,
In a holy rage
For the world to see?
It puzzles the age,
It puzzles me.
It puzzled many
A Desert Father.
And I think it puzzled the Good Lord, rather.

Sister Mary Jean Dorcy, O. P.

POOR BANDAGED CHILDREN OF EVE

Clay is a fallible substance, heir to many blunders. It seems to tempt the Creator, who so well remembers that we are dust, to bring down with a resounding crash anyone who tries to wear too much dignity. So often, like Peter, our words betray us.

Not that words well chosen and neatly fitted together cannot accomplish great things. Thought out discreetly and placed on paper, they may be devastating in their effect. But on the stumbling tongues of Adam's children they often betray us and leave us in the spotlight with all the world laughing at us. Laughter is good for the soul; it is a great help to humility. Who can feel anything but humble, having tripped over the tongue in an attempt to say something very, very seriously? And what is of greater assistance in the matter of pulling "boners" than what Hamlet so feelingly calls "Words, words, words"?

Out of the mouths of babes have come some of the most heart-warming of blunders, without which the lives of teachers would be glum indeed. The pity of it is that teacher is so often allergic to anything like originality in her young charges. It's a disease she contracted in Normal School, and it leaves its mark upon her for life. A child walks blank and unspoiled into her classroom, his mind open, his nerves sound. By every means in her power she strives to complicate his ignorance, until he emerges from college a tattered wreck who no longer sees any possibilities in spelling and has lost all curiosity as to the native haunts of the least common denominator. Bound by iron-walled conventions, he no longer trails clouds of glory; only gnatlike clouds of facts that will add to the annoyances of this harrowing existence: *i* before *e* except after *c*; 6 × 6 *is* 36; the Spanish Armada was defeated in 1588. What a life! No wonder Heaven is for children!

Children alone have the temerity to trifle with the rules that generations of unimaginative adults have laid down. "O my God, make Bismarck the capital of New Hampshire," wrung prayerfully from the heart of a hard-pressed fifth-grader seems no more impossible to the child (perhaps also to God) than some of the more stately petitions He gets from His college-level correspondents. But, grimly entrenched behind her substantial desk, teacher is dead set against such originality. Whether or not she wears a religious habit, she displays the same unbending loyalty to the silent *e* and the proper place for a comma; though it may take years of such teachers to stifle forever one's urge to spell by ear. By the time a youth is out of college, he has had sixteen years of practice with the circumbendibus. He knows a dozen ways of saying a thing gracefully without letting anyone know what he is talking about. But lost—forever lost—is his childhood key to mystery, the direct approach. Life is real, life is earnest. He does not even care who Ernest is any more. And nothing is as it seems; only as the statistical reports reveal.

Consider for one moment the joy of the direct approach. Forget, if you can, the rules of grammar and syntax and arithmetic with which you have blighted so many young lives. Pretend, if you haven't forgotten how, that you are nine years old. Shuffle off the garment of adult flesh. Return to the state of pristine ignorance where you thought Pennsylvania was large and pink, and Vermont small and lavender. Shed decimals, fractions, and compound interest; not to mention income tax. Breathe air uncomplicated by politics, philosophy, or afternoon teas. Look up at the world again, instead of down your nose at it. And there, under the spreading chestnut tree, the village blacksmith stands—of course you remember; Blessed John the Blacksmith and Blessed Michael the Dark Angel!

The ponderous words in which we clothe ideas in this never-too-graceful language so often betray us in our prayers. Here of all places we are dead serious; our poor mischievous mind is on its best behavior. It is no place for levity. Running a close second is the catechism with its completely sober statement of dogma. And yet, with this unpromising material, countless unsung urchins have developed private and hilarious heresies. The most brilliant heresiarchs in history have had to work much harder for results; and gave far less entertainment for their pains.

Some of the connections our children make are more intelligent than we are willing to admit. One prays earnestly, "Give us this day our day-old bread." Not money, not power, not quail-on-toast, but bread—specific, stale, solid, day-old bread. It is something that we, shut from Heaven with a dome more vast, would never think of asking Heaven to give us. And how often we would be telling the truth if we just acknowledged, "O my God, I am partly sorry for having offended Thee. . . ."

You've heard of Gladly—Gladly, the Cross-eyed Bear? It's an old story but ah—how quickly we forget its lesson! You can visualize it yourself; the stiffly starched little girls, the cleaned-and-pressed little boys shined up almost beyond endurance, the Sunday school teacher innocently plunking out the accompaniment as her erring lambs bleat, with all the ardor of young hearts, "Gladly, the Cross-eyed Bear!" You can just bet on it that *she* has never thought of such a beast. She seldom thinks of bears, in fact, except bear and forbear, who probably are not cross eyed. But to her unspoiled little satellites, a cross-eyed bear is just as good a subject for a hymn as a lot of other things people might name.

You learn very early that when a second-grader tiptoes up to your desk and enquires " 'Str, how do you spell AZZITIZ-ZIN—you know, 'Str, 'I will be dumb on earth azzitizzin heaven'?" it's no sign he has a drop of irreverence in his system. If he asks about the Forty Hours' Commotion, you take it calmly. He will just as fervently proclaim, "I plejja legion to the flag on tooth a repub brick where Richard stands; one ration in the visible with liberty and just as for all."

Dolores Whitney is one of those mythical people who exist only in words, like Richard who stands on the republic, life is Ernest, and sudden Sally. At least one child in every generation will get up the courage to ask who she is, and will hopefully repeat, "Hail Mary fulla grace Dolores Whitney," to see if you can identify her. Nobody means any harm by it, but—words, words, words!

The call on a teacher's vocabulary was never greater. She has to have in her head a six-column polyglot edition of what are to her the simplest and most obvious truths, because her words and her children's may be centuries apart. You, for instance, give a dramatic rendition of the Flight into Egypt. Your rapt audience pictures St. Joseph phoning United Airlines, Our Lady packing airway luggage; while you trudge along piously beside the Holy Family across the burning plains of "Egypt's desert bleak and wild," your children have left you far behind and are already landing in Cairo. If you tell them emphatically that the angel told St. Joseph to take Our Lady and *flee* into Egypt, one of your budding naturalists will be sure to bring you the picture from her book and ask you, "If you pleathe, Thithter, where ith the flea?" You can't win.

A classic among the outpourings of uninhibited modern minds is this gem penned—it is sworn by the teacher—by a fourth-grade boy:

THE FLIGHT INTO EGYPT

ACT I: *Bethlehem*

JOSEPH: ZZZZZZZZZZ-ZZZZZZZZ-ZZZZZZZZZZ

MARY: *Zzzzzz-Zzzzzzz-Zzzzzzzz*

JESUS: *zzzzz*

ACT II: *Bethlehem*

ANGEL: Wakest thou, Joseph, you got to takest the Child and His mother and flee-est into Egypt.

JOSEPH: Wakest thou, Mary, we got to takest the Child and flee-est into Egypt.

MARY: Wake up, Jesus.

ACT III: *On the way to Egypt*

JOSEPH: *Silent*

MARY: *Silent*

JESUS: *Silent*

ACT IV: *Egypt*

JOSEPH: Look, Mary, those people are worshipping idols. Isn't that awful?

MARY: Look, Jesus, those people are worshipping idols.

JESUS *looks*.

THE IDOLS: *CRASH! BOOM! BANG!*

The End

While I have seen more than one play that would have profited by a third act like that, you can still see teacher's problem.

God's world is a never-ending source of awe to a child. Fascinated, he watches it unfold its mysteries—ripples in the water, baby ducks, a caterpillar. He is continually bumping himself against the world that man has made. Its furniture is too big for him, its jokes are not funny to him, and he is continually being rebuked for trying to make the best of it. It is a bitter sort of betrayal to find that even words cannot be trusted.

God can be expected to understand all things, so it does not greatly matter that a child cannot, with his limited experience, realize the meaning of the words he uses. He will someday. We who are old enough to be mildly scandalized when a child takes undue liberties with an established formula of prayer sometimes forget that there are two sides to the question. We are the teachers, and it is certainly our business to see that the words he uses are the right ones, even if he does not at the moment understand all their meaning. But ours is the humbler office, after all. We deal only with the letter. It is theirs to teach us with what frank admission of dependence we are to plead our case to a God who can accomplish *anything* if He will. We tell a child dutifully that prayer is a lifting up of the mind and heart to God; *up* is a definite direction to him, and he logically looks *up*, higher than himself, for help. We are older, wiser; scientists have told us there isn't any up, so we measure God's greatness by our littleness, and our prayers do not soar very high at times. They can't; they are fettered to ourselves and to our limited view of what we, personally, think ought to be done. A child realizes that he has limitations—his report card is a standing testimony of it. There are lots of things he knows he doesn't know. To him, everyone from the child in the grade above him to the school principal and on up to God is wiser than he. When he needs help, he has the good sense to ask somebody for it. How many years has it been since we self-sufficient mortals remembered to do that?

Let us pray with the little English girl evacuated from London during the blitz: "Dear God, take care of Daddy and don't let the bombs get him; take care of Mommy and don't let her be scared; and *for heaven's sakes*, God, take care of Yourself. If anything happens to You, WE'RE SUNK!"

May the divine sisters remain always with us, and may the sould of the faithful be parted, through the mercy of God dress in peace. Amen.

Mary Lavin

MY VOCATION

I'm not married yet, but I'm still in hopes. And judging by the way my hopes are itching, I'd say I was never cut out to be a nun in the first place. Anyway, I was only thirteen when I got the Call, and I think if we were living out here in Crumlin at the time, in the new houses that the Government gave us, I'd never have got it at all, because we hardly ever see nuns out here, somehow, and a person wouldn't take so much notice of them out here anyway. It's so airy you know, and they blow along in their big white bonnets and a person wouldn't take any more notice of them than the sea gulls that blow in from the sea. And then, too, you'd never get near enough to them out here to get the smell of them.

It was the smell of them I used to love in the Dorset Street days, when they'd stop us in the street to talk to us when we'd be playing hopscotch on the path. I used to push up as close to them as possible and take great big sniffs of them. But that was nothing to when they come up to the room to see Mother. You'd get it terribly strong then.

"What smell are you talking about?" asked my father one day when I was going on about them after they went. "That's no way to talk about people in Religious Orders," he said. "There's no smell at all off the like of them."

That was right, of course, and I saw where I was wrong. It was the no-smell that I used to get, but there were so many smells fighting for a place in Dorset Street—fried onions, and garbage, and the smell of old rags—that a person with no smell at all stood out a mile from everybody else. Anyone with an eye in their head could see that I didn't mean any disrespect.

It vexed me shockingly to have my father think such a thing. I told him so, too, straight out.

"And if you want to know," I finished up, "I'm going to be a nun myself when I get big."

But my father only roared out laughing.

"Do you hear that?" he said, turning to Mother. "Isn't that a good one? She'll be joining the same order as you, I'm thinking." And he roared out laughing again: a very common laugh I thought, even though he was my father.

And he was nothing to my brother Paudeen.

"We'll be all right if it isn't the Order of Mary Magdalene that one joins," he said.

What do you make of that for commonness? Is it any wonder I wanted to get away from the lot of them?

He was always at me, that fellow, saying that I was cheapening myself, and telling Ma on me if he saw me as much as lift my eye to a fellow passing me in the street.

"She's mad for boys, that one," he used to say. And it wasn't true at all. It wasn't my fault if the boys were always after me, was it? And even if I felt a bit sparky now and then, wasn't that the kind that always became nuns? I never saw a plain-looking one, did you? I never did. Not in those days, I mean. The ones that used to come visiting us in Dorset Street were all gorgeous-looking, with pale faces and not a rotten tooth in their heads. They were twice as good-looking as the Tiller Girls in the Gaiety. And on Holy Thursday, when we were doing the Seven Churches, and we used to cross over the Liffey to the south side to make up the number, I used to go into the Convent of the Reparation just to look at the nuns. You see them inside in a kind of little golden cage back of the altar in their white habits with blue sashes and their big silver beads dangling down by their side. They were like angels: honest to God. You'd be sure of it, if you didn't happen to hear them give an odd cough now and again, or a sneeze.

It was in there with them I'd like to be, but Sis—she's my girl friend—she told me they were all ladies, titled ladies too, some of them, and I'd have to be a lay sister. I wasn't having any of that, thank you. I could have gone away to domestic service any day if that was only all the ambition I had. It would have broken my mother's heart to see me scrubbing floors and the like. She never sank that low, although there were fourteen of them in the family, and only eleven of us. She was never anything less than a wardmaid in the Mater Hospital, and they're sort of nurses, if you like, and when she met my father she was after getting an offer of a great job as a barmaid in Geary's of Parnell Street. She'd never have held with me being a lay sister.

"I don't hold with there being any such thing as lay sisters at all," she said. "They're not allowed a hot jar in their beds, I believe, and they have to sit at the back of the chapel with no red plush on their kneeler. If you ask me, it's a queer thing to see the Church making distinctions."

She had a great regard for the Orders that had no lay sisters at all, like the Little Sisters of the Poor and the Visiting Sisters.

"Oh, they're grand women!" she said.

You'd think then, wouldn't you, that she'd be glad when I decided to join them? But she was as much against me as any of them.

"Is it you?" she cried. "You'd want to get the impudent look taken off your face if that's the case!" she said tightly.

I suppose it was the opposition that nearly drove me mad. It made me dead set on going ahead with the thing.

You see, they never went against me in any of the things I was going to be before that. The time I said I was going to be a Tiller Girl in the Gaiety, you should have seen the way they went on: all of them. They were dead keen on the idea.

"Are you tall enough though—that's the thing?" said Paudeen.

And the tears came into my mother's eyes.

"That's what I always wanted to be when I was a girl," she said, and she dried her eyes and turned to my father. "Do you think there is anyone you could ask to use his influence?" she said. Because she was always sure and certain that influence was the only thing that would get you any job.

But it wasn't influence in the Tiller Girls: it was legs. And I knew that, and my legs were never my strong point, so I gave up that idea.

Then there was the time I thought I'd like to be a waitress, even though I wasn't a blonde.

But you should see the way they went on then too.

"A packet of henna would soon settle the hair question," said Paudeen. And Mother was only worried about my morals.

True, they were doubtful that I'd get any of these jobs, but they didn't raise any obstacles, and they didn't laugh at me like they did in this case.

"And what will I do for money," said my father, "when they come looking for your dowry? If you haven't an education you have to have money going into those convents."

But I turned a dead ear to him.

"The Lord will provide," I said. "If it's His will for me to be a nun He'll find a way out of all difficulties," I said grandly, and in a voice I imagined to be as near as I could make it to the ladylike voices of the Visiting Sisters.

But I hadn't much hope of getting into the Visiting Sisters. To begin with, they always seemed to take it for granted I'd get married.

"I hope you're a good girl," they used to say to me, and you'd know by the way they said it what they meant. "Boys may like a fast girl when it comes to having a good time, but it's the modest girl they pick when it comes to choosing a wife," they said. And suchlike things. They were always harping on the one string. Sure they'd never get over it if I told them what I had in mind. I'd never have the face to tell them!

And then one day what did I see but an advertisement in the paper!

WANTED, POSTULANTS, it said, in big letters, and then underneath, in small letters, there was the address of the Reverend Mother you were to apply to; and in smaller letters still, at the very bottom, were the words that made me sit up and take notice. NO DOWRY, they said.

"That's me," said I, and there and then I up and wrote off to them, without as much as saying a word to anyone, only Sis.

Poor Sis; you should have seen how bad she took it.

"I can't believe it," she said over and over again, and she threw her arms around me and burst out crying. She was always a good sort, Sis.

Every time she looked at me she burst out crying. And I must say that was more like the way I expected people to take me. But as a matter of fact Sis started the ball rolling, and it wasn't long after that everyone began to feel bad, because you see, the next thing that happened was a telegram arrived from the Reverend Mother in answer to my letter.

"It can't be for you," said my mother as she ripped it open. "Who'd be sending you a telegram?"

And I didn't know who could have sent it either until I read the signature. It was Sister Mary Alacoque.

That was the name of the nun in the paper.

"It's for me, all right," I said then. "I wrote to her," I said, and felt a bit awkward.

My mother grabbed back the telegram.

"Glory be to God," she said, but I don't think she meant it as a prayer. "Do you see what it says: calling to see you this afternoon, *Deo Gratias*. What on earth is the meaning of all this?"

"Well!" I said defiantly, "when I told you I was going to be a nun you wouldn't believe me. Maybe you'll believe it when I'm out among the savages!" I added. Because it was a missionary order: that's why they didn't care about the dowry. People are always leaving money in their wills to the Foreign Missions, and you don't need to be too highly educated to teach savages, I suppose.

"Glory be to God," said my mother again. And then she turned on me. "Get up out of that and we'll try and put some sort of front on things before they get here. There'll be two of them, I'll swear: nuns never go out alone. Hurry up, will you?"

Never in your life did you see anyone carry on like my mother did that day. For the few hours that remained of the morning she must have worked like a lunatic, running mad around the room, shoving things under the bed, ramming home the drawers of the chest, and sweeping things off the seats of the chairs.

"They'll want to see a chair they can sit on, anyway," she said. "And I suppose we'll have to offer them a bite to eat."

"Oh, a cup of tea," said my father.

But my mother had very grand ideas at times.

"Oh, I always heard you should give monks and nuns a good meal," she said. "They can eat things out in the world that they can't eat in the convent. As long as you don't ask them. Don't say will you or won't you! Just set it in front of them—that's what I always heard."

I will say this for my mother, she has a sense of occasion, because we never heard any of this lore when the Visiting Sisters called, or even the Begging Sisters, although you'd think they could do with a square meal by the look of them sometimes.

But no: there was never before seen such a fuss as she made on this occasion.

"Run out to Mrs. Mullins in the front room and ask her for the lend of her brass fender," she cried, giving me a push out the door. "And see if poor Mr. Duffy is home from work—he'll be good enough to let us have a chair, I'm sure, the poor soul; the one with the plush seat," she cried, coming out to the landing after me and calling across the well of the stairs.

As I disappeared into Mrs. Mullins' I could see her standing in the doorway as if she was trying to make up her mind about something. And sure enough, when I came out lugging the fender with me, she ran across and took it from me.

"Run down to the return room, like a good child," she said, "and ask old Mrs. Dooley for her tablecloth—the one with the lace edging she got from America." And as I showed some reluctance she caught my arm. "You might give her a wee hint of what's going on. Won't everyone know it as soon as the nuns arrive? And it'll give her the satisfaction of having the news ahead of everyone else."

But it would be hard to say who had the news first, because I was only at the foot of the steps leading to the return room when I could hear doors opening in every direction on our own landing, and the next minute you'd swear they were playing a new kind of postman's knock, in which each one carried a piece of furniture round with him, by the way our friends and neighbors were rushing back and forth across the landing; old Ma Dunne with her cuckoo clock, and young Mrs. Mc-Bride, that shouldn't be carrying heavy things at all, with our old wicker chair that she was going to exchange for the time with a new one of her own. And I believe she wanted to get her piano rolled in to us, too, only there wasn't time!

That was the great thing about Dorset Street: you could meet any and all occasions—you had so many friends at your back. And you could get anything you wanted, all in a few minutes, without anyone outside the landing being any the wiser.

My mother often said it was like one big happy family, that landing—including the return room, of course.

The only thing was, everyone wanted to have a look at the room.

We'll never get shut of them before the nuns arrive, I thought.

"Isn't this the great news entirely!" said old Mrs. Dooley, making her way up the stairs as soon as I told her. And she rushed up to my mother and kissed her. "Not but that you deserve it," she said. "I never knew a priest or nun yet that hadn't a good mother behind them!" And then Mrs. McBride coming out, she drew her into it. "Isn't that so, Mrs. Mc-Bride?" she cried. "I suppose you heard the news?"

"I did indeed," said Mrs. McBride. "Not that I was surprised," she said, but I think she only wanted to let on she was greater with us than she was, because as Sis could tell you, there was nothing of the Holy Molly about me—far from it.

What old Mr. Duffy said was more like what you'd expect.

"Well, doesn't that beat all!" he cried, hearing the news as he came up the last step of the stairs. "Ah, well, I always heard it's the biggest divils that make the best saints, and now I can believe it!"

He was a terribly nice old man.

"And is it the Foreign Missions?" he asked, calling me to one side. "Because if that's the case, I want you to know you can send me raffle tickets for every draw you hold, and I'll sell the lot for you and get the stubs back in good time, with the money along with it in postal orders. And what's more—" he was going on, when Mrs. Mullins let out a scream.

"You didn't tell me it was the Missions," she cried. "Oh, God help you, you poor child!" And she threw up her hands. "How will any of us be saved at all at all with the like of you going to the ends of the earth where you'll never see a living soul only blacks till the day you die! Oh, glory be to God. And to think we never knew who we had in our midst!"

In some ways it was what I expected, but in another way I'd have liked it if they didn't all look at me in such a pitying way.

And old Mrs. Dooley put the lid on it.

"A saint—that's what you are, child," she cried, and she caught my hand and pulled me down close to her—she was a low butt of a little woman. "They tell me it's out to the poor lepers you're going?"

That was the first I heard about lepers, I can tell you. And I partly guessed the poor old thing had picked it up wrong, but all the same I put a knot in my handkerchief to remind me to ask where I was going.

And I may as well admit straight out that I wasn't having anything to do with any lepers. I hadn't thought of backing out of the thing entirely at that time, but I was backing out of it if it was to be lepers!

The thought of the lepers gave me the creeps, I suppose. Did you ever get the feeling when a thing was mentioned that you *had* it? Well, that was the way I felt. I kept going over to the basin behind the screen (Mrs. McBride's) and washing my hands every minute; and as for spitting out, my throat was raw by the time I heard the cab at the door.

"Here they come," cried my father, raising his hand like the starter at the dog track.

"Out of this, all of you," cried Mrs. Mullins, rushing out and giving an example to everyone.

"Holy God!" said my mother, but I don't think that was meant to be a prayer either.

But she had nothing to be uneasy about: the room was gorgeous.

That was another thing: I thought they'd be delighted with the room. We never did it up any way special for the Visiting Sisters, but they were always saying how nice we kept it: maybe that was only to encourage my mother, but all the same it was very nice of them. But when the two Recruiting Officers arrived (it was my father called them that after they went) they didn't seem to notice the room at all in spite of what we'd done to it.

And do you know what I heard one of them say to the other?

"It seems clean, anyway," she said. Now I didn't like that "seems." And what did she mean by the "anyway," I'd like to know?

It sort of put me off from the start—would you believe that? That, and the look of them. They weren't a bit like the Visiting Sisters—or even the Begging Sisters; who all had lovely figures —like statues. One of them was thin, all right, but I didn't like the look of her all the same. She didn't look thin in an ordinary way; she looked worn away, if you know what I mean. And the other one was fat. She was so fat I was afraid if she fell on the stairs she'd start to roll like a ball.

She was the boss: the fat one.

And do you know one of the first things she asked me? You'd never guess. I don't even like to mention it. She caught ahold of my hair.

"I hope you keep it nice and clean," she said.

What do you think of that? I was glad my mother didn't hear her. My mother forgets herself entirely if she's mad about anything. She didn't hear it, though. But I began to think to myself that they must have met some very low-class girls if they had to ask *that* question. And wasn't that what you'd think?

Then the worn-looking one said a queer thing, not to me, but to the other nun.

"She seems strong, anyway," she said. And there again I don't think she meant my health. I couldn't help putting her remark alongside the way she was so worn looking, and I began to think I'd got myself into a nice pickle.

But I was prepared to go through with it all the same. That's me; I have great determination although you mightn't believe it. Sis often says I'd have been well able for the savages if I'd gone on with the thing.

But I didn't.

I missed it by a hairsbreadth, though. I won't tell you all the interview, but at the end of it, anyway, they gave me the name of the convent where I was to go for Probation, and they told me the day to go, and they gave me a list of the clothes I was to get.

"Will you be able to pay for them?" they said, turning to my father. They hadn't taken much notice of him up to that.

I couldn't help admiring the way he answered.

"Well, I managed to pay for plenty of style for her up to now," he said, "and seeing that this mourning outfit is to be the last I'll be asked to pay for, I think I'll manage it all right. Why?"

I admired the "why?"

"Oh, we have to be ready for all eventualities," said the fat one.

Sis and I nearly died laughing afterward, thinking of those words. But I hardly noticed them at the time, because I was on my way out the door to order a cab. They had asked me to get one and they had given me so many instructions that I was nearly daft.

They didn't want a flighty horse, and they didn't want a cab that was too high up off the ground, and I was to pick a cabby that looked respectable.

Now at this time, although there were still cabs to be hired, you didn't have an almighty great choice, and I knew I had my work cut out for me to meet all their requirements.

But I seemed to be dead in luck in more ways than one, because when I went to the cabstand, there among the shiny black cabs, with big black horses that rolled their eyes at me, there was one old cab and it was all battered and green moldy. The cabby, too, looked about as moldy as the cab. And as for the horse—well, wouldn't anyone think that he'd be moldy too? But as a matter of fact the horse wasn't moldy in any way. Indeed, it was due to the way he bucketed it about that the old cab was so racked-looking; it was newer than the others, I believe, and as for the cabby, I believe it was the horse had him so bad-looking. That horse had the heart scalded in him.

But it was only afterward I heard all this. I thought I'd done great work, and I went up and got the nuns and put them into it and off they went, with the thin one waving to me.

It was while I was still waving that I saw the horse starting his capers.

My first thought was to run, but I thought I'd have to face them again, so I didn't do that. Instead, I ran after the cab and shouted to the driver to stop.

Perhaps that was what did the damage. Maybe I drove the horse clean mad altogether, because the next thing he reared up and let his hind legs fly. There was a dreadful crash and a sound of splintering, and the next thing I knew the bottom of the cab came down on the road with a clatter. I suppose it had got such abuse from that animal from time to time it was on the point of giving way all the time.

It was a miracle for them they weren't let down on the road —the two nuns. It was a miracle for me, too, in another way, because if they did I'd have to go and pick them up, and I'd surely be drawn deeper into the whole thing.

But that wasn't what happened. Off went the horse as mad as ever down the street, rearing and leaping, but the nuns must have got a bit of a warning and held onto the sides, because the next thing I saw, along with the set of four feet under the horse, was four more feet showing out under the body of the cab and running for dear life.

Honest to God, I started to laugh. Wasn't that awful? They could have been killed, and I knew it, although as a matter of fact someone caught hold of the old cab before it got to Parnell Street, and they were taken out of it and put into another cab. But once I started to laugh I couldn't stop, and in a way—if you can understand such a thing—I laughed away my vocation. Wasn't that awful?

Not but that I have a great regard for nuns, even to this day, although, mind you, I sometimes think the nuns that are going nowadays are not the same as the nuns that were going in our Dorset Street days. I saw a terribly plain-looking one the other day in Cabra Avenue. But all the same, they're grand women! I'm going to make a point of sending all my kids to school with the nuns, anyway, when I have them. But of course it takes a fellow with a bit of money to educate his kids nowadays. A girl has to have an eye to the future, as I always tell Sis—she's my girl friend, you remember.

Well, we're going out to Dollymount this afternoon, Sis and me, and you'll never know who we'll pick up. So long for the present!

Cornelia Otis Skinner

FAMILY BLESSING

It was heart-warming to attend a recent sailing of that festive craft, the S.S. *Vulcania* bound from New York to Naples with a passenger complement that was nostalgically prewar in character. There were the same wanly exhausted Americans, the same Italians being exuberantly typical, the same wildly running children hurtling themselves into the same gentle-eyed stewards. The same pairs of nuns stood apart, discreetly whispering, and the same energetic priests paced the decks with the same determined vigor. The familiar scene of amiable pandemonium quickened the sentimental pulse and set me turning back the pages of mental scrapbooks to breathless girlhood trips when Italy meant culture and fleas, *gelati* and *carabinieri* officers, tooled-leather picture frames, and, if you had anything left on your letter of credit, a tea gown from Fortuny.

Perhaps it was the glimpse of the black-robed clergy on their way to receive the papal blessing that put me especially in mind of Rome and of a pilgrimage made to that Eternal City during the mid 1920's by my mother, father and self. It was part of the parental scheme for my educational and spiritual improvement that, if possible, we achieve the privilege of having an audience with the Pope. None of us knew exactly how to go about getting it, for we were not of the Faith. It would have been difficult to define just what the family faith was. Mother, baptized a Catholic, but for some reason not brought up as one, wavered between the Episcopal Church "because such nice people went there" and Ethical Culture "because of that wonderful Dr. Adler"; Father, although he was the son of a Universalist preacher, adapted himself with

an actor's sense of theatre to whatever church, temple or even
mosque in which he chanced to find himself . . . not that he
very often did; while I, being at the same time desperately in
love with an actor who was an ardent Christian Scientist, was
temporarily immersed in Mary Baker Eddy. My father,
through his friends in the Catholic Actors' Guild, was able to
pull a few ecclesiastical wires, and we ended up with an official
letter introducing the Skinner family to the head of the American College of Priests in Rome. The fact that the letter was
from Cardinal Hayes awed us all very much. Mother put it,
for safekeeping, along with our passports, which meant that it
got lost quite as often, as Mother, with her sense of infinite
variety, was always finding new places where our passports
could be successfully hidden from everybody, including herself. The final place she had picked out had been the bottom
of my overnight case in which a bottle of Chanel's Gardenia
had come unstoppered, and when we unearthed the precious
document it reeked less of the odor of sanctity than of the
sort of sachet you send your cousin at Christmas. Our stay in
Rome being limited, we were due to deliver the letter that
afternoon. We aired it out as best we could, and by the time
we drove up to the doors of the American College, Mother
optimistically concluded that whoever read it would think it
was incense. A handsome monsignor received us with cordial
dignity, read the pungent communication without either batting an eyelid or dilating a nostril, and told us he would be
most happy to arrange for an audience . . . it might take a
few days . . . he could not say how many . . . but in due
course we would receive our formal invitation from the Vatican. Father thanked him; so did Mother, then added with a
distressed flutter, "I think Your Reverence should know that
we're not Catholics," and at that we all three looked as though
the old story of our each having served a jail sentence had at
last caught up with us. "But," Mother added brightly, "we'd
all like to be!" The monsignor smiled warmly. People always
smiled warmly at Mother. However, he also rose abruptly.
Possibly he figured there would hardly be time for him to

teach us our catechism prior to our audience. With a few kindly assurances to the effect that the papal benediction could extend even to such heretics as we, he politely saw us to the door and down the steps. We clambered into our waiting *carrozza* with the pious expressions of choirboys under the appraising eye of a deacon and, sitting very upright, drove back to our hotel, where with the aid of a few *americanos* sipped in the loggia to the strains of "Valencia," we relaxed into our habitual and more secular manner.

Some two hours later while we were freshening up for dinner, there came an impressive knock on the door which I opened to admit the still more impressive presence of a gigantic individual, startlingly clad in the Michelangelo costume of the Papal Guard. At sight of this magnificent blue-and-white creature in striped doublet and hose I gasped, Mother uttered a breathless "My!" and Father came out with a clarion "Good God!" The dazzling giant handed Father an envelope embossed with the Vatican seal, said something about the "Papa" which, I hissed at my parent, meant Pope not Poppa, bowed and departed. Father opened the envelope, took out a heavy card exquisite with engraving and Spencerian penmanship, studied it for some time, then handed it to Mother with the excuse that he didn't have his glasses. Mother also studied it for a period, then looked up with the triumphant expression of someone who has just broken the enemy code, and said, "Why, it's perfectly simple . . . it's in Latin." Father asked her what it said if it was so simple, to which Mother countered that she hadn't the slightest idea. "But," she said with maternal pride, "Cornelia's just had two years at Bryn Mawr," and she passed the card on to me. My last practice in Latin had been that of memorizing an English trot of the *Aeneid*, which hadn't exactly equipped me for such social emergency as now confronted me.

"This may take a little time," I said, and retired to the bedroom to do my homework, muttering over, as I went, the verbs that take the dative. Be it to the glory of Bryn Mawr that it took only some fifteen concentrated minutes for my

Latin to come back to me (there wasn't much to come), and I returned to my parents with the information that our audience was set for the following morning at 11:30. This didn't give us much time in which to make our preparations; not that we knew what preparations to make. We were aware that there were strict regulations in the matter of clothes, but we were quite vague as to what they were. Mother gave a little moan and said oh dear, what a pity it was we weren't Catholics, an observation she was to repeat at periodic intervals during the ensuing twenty-four hours. We consulted the hotel manager, to whom the dilemma of untutored American Protestants was an old and pretty uninteresting story. The *signor*, came the expressionless patter, could wear *il smoking* . . . dinner jacket and black tie; the *signora* must wear all black . . . high neck, long sleeves, head covering of a black veil; the *signorina* likewise . . . however, the *signorina* might, if she chose, go in all white, as she was still . . . and he coughed discreetly . . . a *signorina*; a blanket observation I considered highly insulting. I was going through my F. Scott Fitzgerald period, and it infuriated me to be considered a virgin, especially when it was perfectly true.

After dinner we started rigging out our individual attire. Father's dinner clothes offered no problem, and Mother claimed that my white tailored sports dress would do nicely augmented with a lace mantilla I had acquired (aping the one I had seen on Lila Lee). I was anything but enthusiastic about this spotless raiment, and when I eventually wore it, did so with an expression that I hope implied there was more in it than met the eye. Outfitting Mother was more involved. The hotel manager had informed her that there was a shop near St. Peter's where they rented out secondhand raincoats to serve in an emergency . . . a suggestion she turned down, saying she didn't think raincoats would be reverent, and besides, she whispered, they might have creatures. Mother's only black dress had a low-cut neck, elbow-length sleeves, and was trimmed with a bright beaded belt, which, in the grotesque fashion of the 1920's, struck her somewhere between the knees

and the bottom of her round little rump. No amount of pin-
ning would close up the space which disclosed an ample ex-
panse of her pretty neck. Father said it must be filled in and
that her sleeves, too, would do well with some lengthening.
Mother found this last bit of advice absurdly superfluous
and asked how the exposure of her forearms could possibly
upset the Pope, to which Father replied that he didn't know,
he'd never been a Pope, but the female regulations called for
long sleeves; and he closed the argument with the actor's
phrase of last resort, "You'll have to fake it." Mother asked
what with and, in a tone of finality, Father answered, "Stuff."

Having on hand, of course, no vestige of "stuff," the only
alternative was to go out early next morning and purchase
some. Leaving Father behind with instructions to get dressed
in his dinner clothes, Mother and I set out in a taxi and rode
to three department stores, all of which proved to be hermeti-
cally closed. The driver eventually offered the slightly belated
explanation that this was Monday and that no shops opened
before noon. He was quite indifferent to our distress until I
explained that we were due for a papal *udienza* and that we
could not possibly go unless we obtained some black material
with which to fill in my mother's neck. In my halting Italian
I think I said "with which to stuff down my mother's throat,"
but he got the idea and was instantly all helpfulness. He had
a friend in the Jewish quarter, he said, the shops there were
open, and he drove us to the establishment of an amiable
little orthodox merchant who obligingly supplied us with two
yards of nun's veiling. Halfway back to the hotel, Mother
suddenly remembered her Catholic acquaintances whose num-
bers were legion and who, she said, would be hurt if she didn't
bring them all rosaries . . . to be sure they probably already
had more than they knew what to do with, still they might
welcome a few freshly blessed ones, and she stopped the taxi
by a catchpenny pavement booth, and amid the conglomera-
tion of mosaic pins and alabaster reproductions of Cupid and
Psyche was able to extricate some two dozen rosaries which
the vendor, deaf to our protests that we were in a hurry and

didn't want them wrapped, insisted upon doing up, each in a little twist of brownish tissue paper, like salt-water taffies.

By the time we returned to our rooms it was after ten thirty. Father, still in drawers and undershirt, was postponing until the last possible moment the embarrassment of putting on a dinner jacket at such a peculiar hour. Mother panted at him for heaven's sake to hurry and get into his clothes, at the same time as she hurried to get out of hers. She had yet to remodel her black dress. With a scant half hour to go, the only expedient was for her to put it on and stand while I sewed in the necessary modesties. Dressmaking was not, along with Latin, one of the equipments for life Bryn Mawr had given me. However, I went to work as best I could, hardly assisted by Mother's inability to remain stationary. The chief cause of her fidgeting was Father, who was still wandering about in a state of unhappiness and seminudity. It seemed he could not locate his studs. Mother suggested a list of likely and unlikely places, and in the end he had to resort to a couple of brass clips pried from the manuscript of his next season's play. Mother thought this somewhat profane, but Father said not at all; it might prove very auspicious.

By dint of some rather cavalier basting and folding under of raw edges, I managed to change Mother's shameless neckline into a demure dickey. My reformation of the forearms was less chic, being some floating attachments that looked like dangling lining. However, we felt sanguine that she would pass the papal censor, except, perhaps, in the matter of the belt of colored beadwork. This was firmly attached to the dress. It seemed a pity to rip it off. On the other hand, it would be a greater pity if, because of such profane frippery, she were to be barred from entrance. She decided to leave the belt as it was, but also, "just in case," she'd carry along some scissors. It was Father who did the carrying . . . the only available scissors being a shearlike pair too large for her handbag. Father patiently stuck them in his dinner-jacket pocket where they clanked musically against his loose change.

Minutes were fleeting and I had still a few gaps to stitch

up. Mother for some time had been urging Father to go down and procure us a *carrozza* . . . a taxi, she felt, would not be sufficiently reverent; and Father kept finding excuses to putter about the room. Finally, mustering her utmost in vehemence, she turned on him and wailed in a fluting tremolo, "Otis, why *don't* you go down and get us a *carrozza?*"

"If you must know, Maud," my Father snapped, "I'm afraid someone'll mistake me for a waiter!" and he strode from the room. I finished sewing Mother in for the duration, we adjusted our respective veils and hastened down to a waiting open carriage in which was sitting my father, looking uncomfortable and remarkably like a waiter. His appearance was further complicated by the fact that he was wearing a pair of black cotton gloves. Mother, at sight of them, emitted a shrill of hysteria and asked what they were for and where he had ever gotten them. He replied that they were for the Pope and that he'd gotten them back in 1919 when he had served as a pallbearer in the funeral of a theatrical manager. Mother's mirth must have weakened his confidence in them, for he took them off with injured dignity and stuffed them in his pocket along with the scissors. We gave our imposing address to the driver, who, upon hearing it, paid tribute to the solemnity of the occasion by whipping up his horse and bolting us down the Corso and over the Tiber with the speed of a bat out of hell. Still clinging to the armrests of the careening vehicle, we came to a stop with a violent jerk before the indicated Vatican doors. Two gorgeous guards admitted us and turned us over to a third, who led us through a labyrinth of marble corridors. Mother began making the little cooing noises she emitted whenever she felt that Father and I were about to do something that would shame us all. She repeated her comment about oh, dear, what a pity it was we weren't Catholic. Then she remembered her collection of rosaries and started taking them out of her bag. They were still done up in the salt-water taffy twists. Feeling that this covering might insulate the beads against proper blessing, she carefully undid each one and hung it on her arm. Then, there being no wastebaskets around the

Vatican, the question arose of how to dispose of the pieces of paper. Mother solved it by doing them up into two puffy wads which she handed to Father with a bland, "Here, dear love." Father, with the expression of an early Christian martyr, jammed them into his pockets along with the shears and the black cotton gloves. His dinner jacket was beginning to take on the appearance of saddlebags.

Our letter from Cardinal Hayes had gained us the special distinction of a semiprivate audience, separate from the larger devotional crowd, in a small salon, the only other occupants of which were two very lovely-looking nuns, obviously persons of considerable ecclesiastical importance. Mother whispered that they were Mother Superiors (one wondered how she knew) and that we must watch them closely and do whatever they did. It didn't seem too practical a suggestion, as that moment both were engaged in intent perusals of their prayer books and we didn't even have a Baedeker among us. Mother compromised by folding her hands before her and staring at them with pious concentration. This embarrassed Father, who put on his reading glasses and walked about the room, examining the pictures in a manner of self-conscious Protestant indifference, which in turn embarrassed me. I stood apart, pretending I didn't know either of them very well. We had not long to wait before a uniformed official appeared, bearing a sort of Malvolio staff, hastily herded us into a row, and told us to get onto our knees. Somehow, in the confusion, the Skinners got separated, so that the final line-up, reading from right to left, turned out to be first Father, then a nun, then myself, then the other nun, and finally Mother, looking more nunlike than the authentic ones. The doors at the right opened to admit the truly impressive entrance of the Pope, wonderfully magnificent in white. He took us in with a brief glance, gave what I presume was a general blessing, then approached us individually, beginning with Father, who, I was ashamed to note, received his benediction with head not bowed in piety, but raised in an attitude of attention that was at least dutiful. I was further mortified to note that when His Holiness extended the great ring, my parent, instead of kissing it, politely shook hands. The next blessing recipient was one of the Mother Superiors, who, with beautiful grace, reached for the gloved finger tip, kissed the ring, crossed herself, and made appropriate response in devotional Latin. It then being my turn, I tried to do as she had done, but in my nervousness I must have clutched the papal hand too intensely, for just as I was about to kiss the ring it was yanked away and the heavy jewel came in contact with an upper tooth from which it excised a neat chip. Horrifying as this was, I did not feel that "I *beg* your pardon!" was the thing to say at the moment; nor did I think it would be seemly to scramble forth and try to salvage the piece of tooth. I let it go as an act of penance. The Pontiff went on with some haste to the second nun, who reacted with the same exquisite dedication as her fellow sister. He then paused before Mother. She kissed the ring most charmingly, crossed herself, and lifted her head in the manner of St. Cecilia having a particularly good vision. The Pope spoke his words of benediction, and to my amazement I heard Mother responding with a stream of little unintelligible sounds . . . not words exactly, just low musical syllables. I thought perhaps that the awesomeness of the ceremony had overworked her volatile emotions and that she had temporarily gone a bit daft. However, the Pope did not appear to think so. He paused, listened, smiled, and gave her an additional blessing before continuing on to other devotees in the adjoining room.

As soon as we got outside I asked my mother what on earth it was she had said in her response. "Nothing," she answered. "It was just because I was so ashamed of us all. There were those two nuns looking so lovely and saying such beautiful things in Latin, and we Skinners looking so hick and saying nothing, so I decided to make noises that sounded like Latin . . . and if the Pope didn't understand, he'd put it down to an American accent. But I think he understood." And the curious thing is, I believe he did.

John McNulty

CAN'T SLIP ANY DRUGS TO SISTERS
ON FIFTH AVENUE

A nun stumbled on the sidewalk on Fifth Avenue, near Forty-seventh Street. There was a bad place in the sidewalk and the nun had stepped on it while walking along with another nun. This happened in the middle of a busy afternoon, and the sidewalks were crowded.

A man in a yellow polo coat grabbed the nun's arm helpfully. The other nun grasped her other arm and looked into her face, which was pale. The two nuns were not used to crowds and milling around, and both looked scared over the trivial mishap.

The man jerked his hat off before he spoke, solicitously, to the nun who had stumbled. He had a cauliflower ear and his hat was a Madison Square Garden kind of hat.

"Is something the matter, Sister?" he said, leaning toward the nun. "Something happen? You hurt yourself, Sister?"

The nun spoke so softly, out of embarrassment, that the man could not hear what she said. Another man, with his hat off, was there by then, and the two nuns and two men made a small clump in the middle of the busy sidewalk. Still another man stood still, only a few feet away, watching them.

"Begging your pardon, Sister," the cauliflower-ear man said, being very careful to use the highest-class language he could figure out, "I thought something happened; you're like in distress. I mean taken or something; or hurt your foot, if you'll excuse me."

From under the black hood and starched linen of her religious garb, the nun looked timidly and kindly at him. "I—I—I slipped," she said, and looked appealingly at the other nun.

"I think Sister is all right now," the other nun said. "Her foot slipped, I think. Are you all right, Sister Veronica?"

"Yes, I twisted my—I twisted my ankle a little," Sister Veronica answered. She took a step or two carefully. The cauliflower-ear man put on his hat, helped her that step or two, then let go of her arm and took his hat off as the two nuns went on slowly and anxiously down the avenue.

"I think she's all right," the second man said to him.

"Jeez, I thought something happen to her, I don't know what," said the cauliflower-ear man. He put on his hat again, looking back at the departing nuns, then started up the street, almost in stride with the second man.

At that minute the third man, the onlooker, joined them, and the three moved along, almost as if they had known each other before this.

"Look, see what I got—amyl nitrite," the third man said, opening his gloved hand and showing a capsule in it. "I was just going to slip it to her if she—"

"Slip what to her?" the cauliflower-ear man said, almost angrily, checking his stride.

"The amyl nitrite," the fellow answered. "I have it for my old man. He gets attacks. He got a bad heart, my old man, so I have to have it, and I was right there. I thought the nun maybe had a heart at—"

"Whaddaya mean, slip it to her? You ain't going to slip no amble nitrites to her," the cauliflower-ear man said. "You ain't slipping no drugs to no nuns on Fifth Avenue. Whaddaya mean?"

"My father," the fellow said, and by now all three were walking together again up the sidewalk, "he's liable to collapse any minute while I'm with him. So I got this—look, it's to keep your heart going if you get a heart attack like my father does." He showed the capsule again and then put it back in his coat pocket.

"Yeh, I know what he means," said the other man. "He thought maybe the sister had a heart attack, and he wanted—"

"Oh, oh," the cauliflower-ear man said, but only partly satisfied, it seemed, by the tone of his voice and the way he looked at the amyl-nitrite man.

"Oh, yes. Yes, that's what I thought. She maybe had a heart attack when I saw you two there helping her. I meant I was ready to slip her the amyl nitrite and bring her to," the man said.

"Yuh? But what if it wasn't?" the cauliflower-ear man asked, only a little placated. "Maybe something else instead of heart attack, and that stuff be exactly the wrong thing to slip her? I don't like the idea, slipping drugs to sisters on Fifth Avenue. You can't go slipping drugs to sisters on Fifth Avenue, what I mean."

"I can tell if it would be the right thing," the man said. "My father—"

"I see't you mean, you meant well all right, but I don't like the idea slipping even well-meant drugs to a sister on Fifth Avenue," the cauliflower-ear man said. Then, just before he turned, he summed it up. "Anyway, the sister made out all right. All's well ends well."

"Yeah. So long," the amyl-nitrite man said, turning the other way at the corner. "Just the same, lucky I was there, in case it was a heart attack. That stuff I showed you save my old man's life many a time. So long."

The cauliflower-ear man went west, the amyl-nitrite man went east, and the third man went straight on up the avenue, looking back; but there was no sign of the two nuns, who were a couple blocks away by then, probably.

St. John Ervine

THE BURIAL

The funeral procession from the girl's home to the graveyard was due to begin at half-past two, but long before that hour the crowd of mourners began to collect. They stood about the entrance to the lane leading to the churchyard, and waited. The home of the dead girl faced the lane, and the procession, therefore, would reach its journey's end in a few moments from the time when it began to move. Townsmen and neighbours mingled with men from the country and the hills and fishermen from the bay where the girl was drowned; and each man, as he came up to a group of his acquaintances, spoke of the terribleness of the disaster, and then the talk circled round the affairs of the small town.

John Mawhinney came along the old road to Ballyshannon, and when he was by the lane he hailed James O'Hara.

"How're ye, James?" he said.

James O'Hara, a lean, foxy-looking man, turned at the sound of Mawhinney's voice. "Och, I'm just middlin'," he replied, "I've the quare cowl on me! How is yourself?"

"Ah, I'm not so bad. Man-a-dear, this is a tarr'ble sad thing about this young girl!"

"Aye, it is that. Man, I mind her when she was that height, the same wee girl!" He allowed his hand to fall to the level of his knees as he spoke. "An' a smart wee girl she was, too! Aye! She always had an answer for ye, whatever ye said, she was that sharp!"

He looked up as he spoke, and saw John McClurg approaching. "Is that you, John?" he said.

McClurg, a large, moon-faced man with little, smiling eyes, came puffing up to them.

"It is surely," he replied to O'Hara's greeting.

"I saw ye in the market the fair day," said Mawhinney, "but ye wurn't lukkin', an' ye didden see me. Did ye do well wi' yer cattle?"

"Ah, I didden do so bad. I might 'a' done better, an' I might 'a' done worse!"

"Did ye sell thon wee heifer ye had wi' ye?"

"I did not. I wudden take the price—"

O'Hara tapped him on the arm. "I s'pose ye come to the funer'l?" he said.

John McClurg glanced across the road to the door of the house where the dead girl lay. "Well," he said, "I thought I wud just dander into the town an' show me respect til the dead. God rest her sowl!" The three men raised their hats at his prayer. "What time does it begin?" he asked.

"They wur talkin' about half-after-two," replied Mawhinney, "but I'm thinkin' it'll be later'n that. Sure, the mail train's not in thrum Bilfast yet, an' there's fren's comin' thrum there an' thrum Derry, too, an' they'll be wantin' their denner when they git here. It'll be three o'clock afore iver they stir out o' the dure!"

"Aye, it will that," said James O'Hara, and then he turned and spoke to John McClurg. "Wur ye wantin' much for yer wee heifer?" he asked.

McClurg bit a piece of tobacco off a long twist of dark villainous stuff, and when he had chewed it in his mouth a while, he spat yellow juice over the kerb, and then said: "You might think I was wantin' too much, an' I might think meself I was wantin' too little!"

"I saw her meself," exclaimed Mawhinney, "afore she went intil the sea, laughin' an' jokin' like annythin'! Aw, God save us all thrum a death the like o' her death!"

"They wur a quare long time findin' her!"

"They wur."

"Wud ye be wantin' five poun's fur yer wee heifer, John McClurg?" said James O'Hara.

"I wud, indeed, an' a bit more on top of it!"

"They foun' her jus' where she went down," continued Mawhinney in the voice of a man who is reciting an oft-told tale. "Man, it's quare the way the body returns like that!"

"Aye!"

"Who's thon man wi' the tall hat an' the long coat on him, d'ye know?" asked one that stood by of Mawhinney as a man in a frock-coat knocked at the door.

"I nivir seen him afore," replied Mawhinney. "He's a stranger in this town, I'm thinkin'. D'ye know him, James?"

"I do not," replied O'Hara. "Mebbe he's come be the train. The mail's in now. Thonder's Patrick Magrath with the mail-car comin' roun' the corner!"

"Ye're mebbe right!" Mawhinney resumed the recital of his tale. "Did ye see the piece in the Derry paper about her?" he said. "Thon was the quare bit. An' there was a piece of portry be the young wumman in the post-affice!"

"Aye, I saw that. It was quare an' nice. I didden know thon wumman cud do the like o' that!"

"Ah, sure she's in Government sarvice, issen she . . . ?"

"The paper said she was the quare, clivir, wee girl, an' tuk a lotta prizes at the school in Derry her da sent her to. They must 'a' spent a power o' money on her trainin'!"

"They did that. They nivir grudged her nathin'. It's a quare pity of them!"

"Aye, it only shows ye shudden make a god of yer childher . . . !"

Two young men, one of whom carried a costly wreath in his hands, went up to the door, and presently were admitted to the house.

"Fur dear sake, luk at thon wreath!" exclaimed John Mawhinney. "Man, thon must 'a' cost somethin'!"

"Aye, it's thrum the young men at the Y.M.C.A. She was goin' to be married to one o' them. Did ye nivir hear about it?"

"Naw. What was his name?"

"I think it wus young McCracken!"

"What! Thon lad?"

"Aye. It'll be a cut-up for him, this . . . ! John McClurg, will ye take six poun' ten for yer heifer?"

"Mebbe I wud if it was affered to me . . . !"

"There's many a Cathlik would be willin' to give a wreath, too, I'm thinkin'!" said John Mawhinney.

"Aye, that's true enough. Sure, there's no room for bigitry where death is! . . . Wur ye thinkin' o' makin' me the affer, James?"

O'Hara walked a little way from the group, and then, squirting tobacco juice before him, returned to it. "Ah, I was just wondherin' if ye wud take it if it was affered t' ye. I wudden affer more'n five poun' for it meself . . . !"

"Ah, well, it wudden be no good you afferin' that amount. I wudden part wi' it fur the money!"

"There's a brave crowd here now," said O'Hara, turning toward the crowd. "It'll be a big procession, I'm thinkin'!"

"It will that. But I've seen bigger. There was the time Dr. Cochrane died. D'ye mind that? That was a procession an' a half!"

"Aye, it was indeed. Near a mile long that was . . . !"

The door of the house opened, and a number of persons entered.

"They'll be startin' soon," said Mawhinney.

"Ah, well, God help her, she'll soon be oura all this. It's the long sleep til the Day o' Judgement!"

"Ye're right there. Ye are indeed . . . !"

The door slowly reopened, and men came forth bearing the yellow coffin on their shoulders. A great quietness descended upon the village street, and each man in it removed his hat and, if he were a Catholic, crossed himself and prayed for the repose of the dead girl's soul. Here and there a woman wrapped her shawl about her face and wept. The bearers carried the coffin across the street to the lane leading to the churchyard, and the people in the street fell in behind and marched slowly toward the grave. A bell tolled softly, and in the house from which the body had just been borne a woman was heard crying and lamenting.

"I'll give ye six poun's fur yer wee heifer," said James O'Hara, as the body went by.

"Ah, God rest her sowl!" murmured McClurg, marking himself with the sign of the cross on the head and breast. "I cudden take less nor six poun' ten!"

"I cudden give more nor six poun' . . . !"

"Well, ye'll not get it fur the price. It's six poun' ten or nathin'!"

"Ye're the hard man to bargain wi' . . . !"

"I'm not hard at all . . . ! Mebbe, they're better dead young nor dead oul'!"

"Will ye not budge yer price?"

"I will not!"

"They're in the graveyard now. . . . Come on down til Maloney's public house, an' I'll sale the bargain wi' ye."

Bruce Marshall

THEIR FIRST MOVIE

It was in 1910 that the first cinema came to the town. Paolo
Sarno took a chance on things and converted the old bus
stables next his ice-cream shop, which was bang opposite the
site on which Father Smith had already built the skeleton of
his new tin church. The priest could see the advertisements
from his presbytery window. They changed twice a week, too,
on Mondays and Thursdays: sometimes they were about a
man called John Bunny and sometimes they were about two
men called Gerald Ames and Stewart Rome, but the advertisement saying that afternoon tea would be served free of charge
to patrons between three and four was always the same. People said that it was rather sporting of Sarno to be so enterpris-
ing, because the craze mightn't last any longer than the one
for rollerskating in which the Italian had taken such a hard
knock two years ago.

The canons of the chapter of the pro-Cathedral, however,
didn't think it sporting at all. They were perturbed because
weekday attendances at Benediction of the Blessed Sacrament
began to fall off and the evening devotions in the month of
May were performed only by the elderly, and even some of
them hadn't been above popping in for an hour's Vitagraph
and a wee free tea during the holy season of Lent when they
thought none of the priests were looking. It was in vain that
Monsignor O'Duffy had thundered from the pulpit, "It's no
by sitting in red plush airmchairs watching a lot of silly gowks
sauntering and daundering about a lot of helterskeltering mov-
ing-picture postcairds that any of ye'll ever see the bonny
Blessed Virgin Mary face to face in the kingdom of Heaven";
the attendances at Benediction during the month of the Sacred

Heart were as poor as during the month of May. Some of the canons at the chapter meeting maintained that it would be more prudent not to condemn the cinema until His Holiness Pope Pius X had made an official pronouncement, but Monsignor O'Duffy had said that that was all havers and clavers and nonsense, and that if they had to wait on an official verdict of the Church, they might be argy-bargying till Doomsday, and that the Church had taken nearly nineteen hundred years to make up its mind about the doctrine of the Immaculate Conception and that they couldn't afford to dilly and dally like that while young folk aye and auld folk, too, were walking straight into the jaws of hell at sixpence a time and children at half price.

It was decided, therefore, to send a deputation to attend a performance. This was possible because, as Monsignor O'Duffy pointed out, although local ecclesiastical law forbade priests to attend theatrical performances, the cinematograph was a very different cup of tea, indeed, and so could not be held to fall within the ban. He said, too, that if the members of the chapter didn't mind, he intended to go himself, as there was no cleric in the diocese who knew more about wickedness than he did, and that he would take his old friends the Reverend Fathers Bonnyboat and Smith with him, because it wouldn't be fair on Signor Sarno to be letting only austere and wise canons have a peek at his newfangled toboggan slide down to the depths of the nethermost pit.

Paolo Sarno seemed to have heard of their intended visit, for he was there in the vestibule to greet them, standing underneath a large framed photograph of a lady called Flora Finch. Father Smith wondered why he hadn't come right out into the street, because that would have been even more polite, but Father Bonnyboat said that he mightn't have heard of their intended visit at all and that it was just by chance that he was standing there, and Monsignor O'Duffy said it was only because he couldn't very well have let them pay for themselves through yon wee hole in the wall into the lassie's face if he had come right out on the pavement, ha, ha. Anyway there he was on the purple carpet, with his thick light-brown fingers looking just like the advertisement for Palethorpe's sausages on the railway embankment.

"*Buon giorno, reverendissimi signori,*" he greeted, because he thought they all spoke Italian. The priests said "*Buon giorno,*" back, except Father Bonnyboat, who had studied in the Scots College in Valladolid instead of the Scots College in Rome, and who said, "*Buenos dias,*" instead. This made Paolo Sarno laugh and say: "*Per Bacco!* The *reverendo* father speaka the Italian like a Spanish cow, *vero*, no offence meant, *reverendo* father. You coma to see my show. Very good, very elevating, very pious. The *reverendi* fathers coma tis way."

The *reverendi* fathers came this way, carrying their inverted black hats in front of their faces like soup plates, and as they trooped along, Monsignor O'Duffy said to Paolo Sarno in a loud voice: "Wicked or elevating, shameful or pious, this new craze'll no last, Mr. Sarno, and in my opinion you'd have done much better to open one of yon miniature shooting ranges with wee celluloid balls dancing about on jets of water, which are without the suspicion of sin."

It took Father Smith's eyes some little time to grow accustomed to the darkness, so that at first he seemed to be sitting in an immense black hole with Father Bonnyboat's overcoat on one side of him and Monsignor O'Duffy's on the other. Gradually, however, the darkness lightened to an amber haze in which he could make out lines of heads all about him like rows of chocolates in a box. On the screen they were showing a blue river meandering along beneath green bridges and an old mouldering church or two, which didn't seem to Father Smith very wicked, because the old mouldering churches were almost certainly Catholic churches with the Body of God safe inside them, and a piano was playing away most politely, tra-la-la-la-la-la.

The same thought must have struck Father Bonnyboat, for he said across Father Smith to Monsignor O'Duffy, "Nothing very irreverent about that, Monsignor."

"Just you wait till we get to the acting," Monsignor O'Duffy said. "They tell me it's worse than yon machines you turn the handles on and look down on piers." He brought his ear very close to Father Smith's and whispered: "Tights. Tell him," he said.

But before Father Smith could pass this information on to Father Bonnyboat, a hat with a large pin stuck through it in the row in front of them turned around and said "*Sssh*," and Father Smith was left to wonder in silence how Monsignor O'Duffy knew so much about what was inside the machines you looked down and turned the handles on on piers. Then the piano suddenly stopped playing and there was a noise in the air just like the buzzing the rotary brush made in the barber's, and the green bridges and the mouldering old churches went on for a moment or two and then they stopped, too, and the lights went up and the rows of heads in front of Father Smith had ears on them and the screen turned out to be not a hung-up sheet at all, but hard and rectangular and glossy with high lights on it here and there as though the paint had run.

"Most edifying, really," Father Bonnyboat said.

"Just you wait, I tell you," Monsignor O'Duffy said.

The lights went down again. This time the film was about a convict in prison. The convict wore a uniform striped broadly like a football jersey, and at first Father Smith was very sorry for him because he seemed to be so miserable. But then the convict escaped and ran around a lot of street corners, and the policemen ran around a lot of street corners after him, but the convict always managed to escape, even when the policemen came at him from both directions at once, because he dodged behind doorways and the policemen ran into one another and knocked one another over. When Father Smith laughed he knew he wasn't doing anything wrong, because he could hear Monsignor O'Duffy and Father Bonnyboat laughing too.

Then the convict ran along a beach, and there were a lot of pretty girls in bathing dresses eating chocolates on the sand, and the convict ran in among them and upset the chocolates, and Father Smith was wondering what Monsignor O'Duffy was going to say about the bathing dresses, when down the gangway came a flashlight crying, "Chocleets, cigarettes and matches." Then the flashlight turned into Angus McNab's face above two sprays of gold buttons leaning across Monsignor O'Duffy's waistcoat and saying to Father Smith, "Do ye no ken me, Father?" One of my altar boys, Father Smith was going to explain to Monsignor O'Duffy, but up on the screen the policeman and the convict and the pretty girls were throwing tarts and pies at one another's faces, and Monsignor O'Duffy was laughing too hard to be able to listen. The pie throwing didn't seem very funny to Father Smith, and it didn't appear to strike Father Bonnyboat as very funny, either, but the rest of the audience roared their heads off and Monsignor O'Duffy laughed enough for both of them.

"Yon fellow's a right comic and no mistake," he said as he sat wiping the tears from his eyes. Then he caught sight of a pretty waitress in a black frock and frisk of apron coming up the gangway. "Hi, lassie, what about yon free tea?" he asked.

"It'll be served during *Death or Dishonour*, sir," she said.

And served during *Death or Dishonour* their tea was, right bang in the middle of the Sheriff's speech, "Boys I kinda reckon there's been dirty work at Red Gulch and we're going to put out that dirty skunk of a double-crossing horse thief Ned Tranter's lights for him so that our God-fearing womenfolk can sleep safe in their beds o' nights and our maidens wander happy and careless 'neath a myriad stars," flashed across the screen just like that, without any commas, but with lots of dots at the end to make up. There was a tray for each, with a teapot and a cup and saucer and two hard little biscuits with ribs running along the back. Monsignor O'Duffy said that if the management had wanted to do things really well they would have given them a boiled egg to their teas as well, but he seemed to enjoy the biscuits all right, soaking them in his cup of tea before he ate them and making great appreciative gurglings, champings, and suckings.

On the screen, above the cups of tea, Ned Tranter had captured the Sheriff's pretty daughter, lassoing her while she was saying her prayers by her bedside and riding off with her on his horse to his mountain fastness. "Ned Tranter," she said to him in a great paragraph through her gag, "you may starve me, beat me, flay me, but never shall I consent to befoul God's great gift of love by becoming the mother of your children, nay, nor shall I cook for you, sew for you, dust for you. Death rather than Dishonour, Ned Tranter, for my heart belongs to clean-limbed Patrick Hogan of Lone Ranch." At this there was a great cheering and clapping and stamping of feet, and Father Bonnyboat said that with a name like that Patrick Hogan must surely be a Catholic, and Monsignor O'Duffy said that just showed ye that even on the fillums the great Holy Kartholic Churrch played a royal and triumphant role. Father Smith was too intrigued with the drama to say anything. With eager eyes and beating heart he watched the Sheriff and Patrick Hogan and the other boys of Red Gulch set out to rescue Molly Kintyre, whose eyes were like forest pools with the ineffable glory of the stars mirrored in their purple depths, at least that was what Patrick Hogan had said when he was playing snooker in a saloon bar with Mickey Riley.

As they set out on horseback they all fired their pistols into the air to let Molly Kintyre know that they were coming, but of course Ned Tranter didn't hear, because he always slept with his dirty head under the blankets. Up hill and down dale they rode, firing their pistols all the time. Sometimes it looked very much as though they were riding up the same hill twice, but Father Smith was too excited to care. With the others he clapped, groaned, lost heart, and clapped again, but at last it was all over and Molly Kintyre was restored to the arms of Patrick Hogan, who swore, colleen bawn, that he would never play snooker in saloon bars again, and the Sheriff said, pointing his revolver at Ned Tranter: "Nix on the gunplay, Tranter. Put 'em up. You're cornered."

The three priests clapped with the rest of the audience, and Father Bonnyboat said that he hadn't seen anything so edifying for a very long time indeed, and Monsignor O'Duffy said that he was never afraid to confess when he was wrong and that it looked very much as though he had been wrong in what he had said about the cinema, and that if the remainder of the programme contained no unpleasant surprises, he would have to make amends to Signor Sarno by buying tickets for all the members of Saint Vincent de Paul Society.

There was, however, no remainder of the programme, for, as soon as the lights were lowered, the blue river and the green bridges and the mouldering old churches started all over again, with the piano going tra-la-la-la-la-la and all. Father Bonnyboat said that he supposed that they really ought to be going, but Monsignor O'Duffy said that that was all havers and nonsense and that "continuous performance" meant that folks could stay in as long as they liked and that he was going to see yon bit again where they threw pies at one another, but that of course Father Bonnyboat and Father Smith could do what they liked. Even when, at the end of the blue river and the mouldering churches, they flashed an orange notice on the screen, PATRONS WHO HAVE SEEN THE FULL PROGRAMME ONCE ARE REQUESTED TO VACATE THEIR SEATS IN FAVOUR OF THOSE WAITING FOR ADMISSION, even then he still held out, maintaining that it wasn't as though he were trying to get served with an extra free tea, but only that he wanted to see them fling yon pies again. But when he had seen them flinging the pies he found that he wanted to see them setting out to round up Ned Tranter again as well, so they all stayed to the end of *Death or Dishonour* and tried not to think that the spectators standing up in the passage were staring at them.

"Of course, it's just a craze and it'll no last," Monsignor O'Duffy said when they stood outside again on the unenchanted pavement.

Father Bonnyboat said that he thought somehow that it was more than a craze, and even wondered whether the blessed in heaven might not be treated to a similar entertainment, since it was so uplifting; but Father Smith said that in heaven the blessed would have our Lord to look at and that nothing could be more uplifting than that. Whereupon they all took off their hats, saluting the priesthood that was in one another, and went back to their churches, because it was the first Thursday of the month and they had confessions to hear.

Arthur J. Roth

MISSION COMPLETED
(from *What Is the Stars?*)

The Slater was no sooner out of one trouble than he was into another. As the Knave had foreseen, the command legal officer threw out the request for a court-martial and the dumb-insolence charge was dropped. The Slater was not one to gloat over a tactical victory. He sportingly applied for a weekend pass and three days' annual leave; requests that were promptly turned down by the adjutant. The Slater simply couldn't be spared from his duties. To prove his point, Percy instituted a new series of reports and invented other clerical duties to keep the Slater busy. For a while the Slater kept up with the overload, but eventually both men tired of the situation and an unspoken truce was established.

The truce was broken early in May, the month of the Blessed Virgin, when the annual mission came to the barracks. For two weeks a pair of cadaverous Passionist Fathers had the whole complement of the post at their mercy. Eloquent men, they took turns in depicting the exquisite pain of broiling on the hot bobs of hell for all eternity. They had an awesome theatrical range. One would shoot a terrifying bony finger at the congregation and roar, "You crucified Him with your sins!" The other would dramatically wipe his brow with a black silk handkerchief, lower his voice to a seductive intensity, and whisper, "Come back to Him." They thundered and threatened, harangued and pleaded, but few came back. The general apathy was put down by the Passionists to a new low of degradation or a new height of corruption, or a combination of both. The truth is that the missioners were fighting not the devil but the weather. The good priests tried hard, but May is the wrong month for a mission. Warm, flower-happy breezes stole tantalizingly through the church. From the voluptuous murmur of the river outside came promises of foot-long trout and voraciously gullible pike. It is astonishing how far a girl's laugh will carry on a May evening. On the second night of the mission a girl laughed softly in Irishtown, a thousand yards distant, and every man in the church heard her. November or December, or even March, might be good months for a mission, but never the month of May. In May even the spirit is weak.

Officially it was a duty parade for the men to march in formation to the church and enter, but once inside they were considered off duty for the rest of the evening, and when the hour-long sermon was over they usually drifted back to the barracks or wandered about the town. The army maintained the right to order a duty parade to any particular point it wished. They were not forcing the men to attend church but merely making it a duty to march to the church door in formation. Of course the men were never informed of this technicality, and practically all of them assumed that they were on duty until the end of the sermon. Which is exactly what the army and the Passionate Fathers wanted. But neither the military nor the clergy reckoned on the Knave, who instituted a thorough study of army regulations and handed down a considered opinion to the effect that the men couldn't be forced to sit through the ceremony. On the third night of the mission he, the Slater, and Fitz stood up in their seats and left the church as the sermon was about to start. No action was taken against them. Word of such an interesting maneouvre was impossible to keep secret, and the next night almost half of the ordnance company walked out. The following morning Lieutenant Pettigo called the Slater into his office. "Were you at the mission?" he asked.

"I was, sir."

"I see." Percy assumed a confidential and thoughtful pose. "It was a grand sermon, was it not?"

The Slater was canny enough not to fall for such an obvious

question. "Did you think so, sir?" he said brightly, after a second's hesitation.

"I did." Pettigo smiled and tried another gambit. "What did *you* think of the sermon, McGurk?"

Once more the Slater attempted to stall. "I really couldn't say, sir," he said, his answer implying that religious sermons were somewhat over his head.

"You couldn't say. Tell me, did you hear the sermon at all?"

"No, sir."

"Why not?"

"I left the church as the sermon was starting."

"You didn't approve of the subject?" the adjutant asked, lapsing into his habitual sarcasm.

"Well, sir, when the parade was dismissed at the church door I considered myself off duty and free to leave."

"Did you now? That's very interesting. I suppose there were others who felt the same way?"

"There were, sir."

"Ordnance men?"

"I didn't notice anyone in particular, sir."

"Well, I have a little duty for you now, McGurk. I want you to stay during the sermon for the rest of the week and take the names of any ordnance men who leave."

"Is that an order, sir?"

Pettigo's face tightened. "That's an order," he affirmed thinly.

"Very good, sir."

The shrewdness of the plan struck the Slater right away. He either had to inform on his friends or let them know of his new duty, in which event they would be forced to stay for the whole service. After dinner he gathered with the Knave and Fitz in the barrack room and told them of his conversation with the adjutant.

"A tricky man," said the Knave, almost in admiration. "There's no flies on Percy."

"Ah, well," Fitz said with righteous disgust. "We're bloody

misfortunate men. The army trains us to kill and the clergy wants us to lay down with the lambs."

"The clergy has this country filled with a sort of nervous sanctity," the Knave commented.

"God knows but they have it easy. The Irish are gifted at doing penance for sins they haven't even committed," Fitz agreed sombrely.

"Did you hear the moans of your man last night about the terrible temptation of women?" the Slater asked.

Fitz snorted with amusement. "It's little that priest knows about Irishwomen. I mind courting a girl in a hay shed one night in Wicklow, and I accidently let my hand rest on her creamery cans. 'You can't do that,' says she to me. 'Why?' says I with an innocent look. 'I'm the temple of the Holy Ghost,' she says." Fitz grinned at the recollection.

"What will we do about tonight?" the Knave asked, bringing the subject back to a practical plane.

"I could go sick this evening, just before the parade," the Slater offered.

"Hopeless," Fitz objected. "You're only supposed to go sick on the morning sick call. You can't go sick in the evenings unless it's an emergency."

"I'll break your arm," the Knave volunteered.

A short silence fell as each man examined the problem. Finally Fitz suggested, "Why don't we keep leaving when the sermon starts? What can he do?"

"He can't charge us with anything," the Knave answered. "But we'd find ourselves on a lot of extra guard duty and fire picket and weekend work details."

"I wonder why he doesn't get one of the N.C.O.'s to take the names?" Fitz asked.

"That wouldn't suit Percy at all," the Knave replied. "He doesn't have a legal leg to stand on. If he had, he'd order us to stay during the sermon. He can't fall back on army regulations. He has to make us defeat ourselves. That's the sort of the twisted bugger." The Knave wasn't concerned whether or not he had to attend the mission. It was the legal aspect of the situation that challenged him. His mind began delicately probing at the problem, and he soon discovered a promising loophole. "Why don't you change your religion?" he asked. "They can't make you enter the church if you're a Mohammedan or Whirling Hindoo or something like that."

"Change my religion?" the Slater echoed in wonder.

"What harm? If you play your cards right you can change back to Catholic when the mission's over."

"What will I change to?"

"Protestant?" the Knave suggested nervously.

"My God, that's heresy," the Slater breathed in horror.

"But only for a couple of weeks," the Knave appealed.

"And, O Thou of the Covetous Eye, what good would it do?" Fitz asked. "Suppose the Slater does change his religion? Percy will only detail you or me to take the names."

"Well, then, we'll change our religion too," the Knave answered. "It isn't the change will make much difference—it's the ramifications. Man alive, think of the flustering uproar that will go on in command when three notifications of a change of religion come from the ordnance corps. There'll be the holy old weeping and wailing over that. Yis, and maybe His Eminence the Cardinal will talk to His Apostolic Reverence the Papal Nuncio, and the both of them up half the night writing petitions in Latin to St. Peter's in Rome. It'll be the sad day for Percy when he chances raising that kind of a dispute with the Vatican."

"I won't be a Protestant," the Slater said stubbornly. Being from the North of Ireland, he was remarkably touchy about Protestants.

"You don't have to change to a new religion," Fitz said. "Submit an application to have your religion changed on your records from Roman Catholic to atheist. Just tell everybody that you've lost the faith."

"That's a great deal better," the Slater admitted with relief. "I wouldn't want to commit heresy, you know. Hell isn't hot enough for them that turn Protestant."

"I'm disappointed," Fitz satirized. "For a moment I had

hopes that the Reformation had finally come to Ireland."

The Slater doubtfully shook his head. "After fighting seven hundred years for freedom to practise our religion—here I am denying it. I'll be damned but that's almost treason." With heresy on one side and treason on the other, he was walking a precariously thin line.

"But that's just it," Fitz argued. "We fought for the freedom to practise it. If we have the freedom to practise it, we also have the freedom not to practise it."

"Oh, but he'll be the great old sinner. What's a little kifuffling or slitting a throat compared to denying your God?" the Knave said to Fitz in an appeal to witness the wonderful depravity of their friend. "I've a good mind to join him." He sighed wistfully, indicating that only his want of courage prevented him from following the Slater's example.

"I'll do it," the Slater affirmed, carried away with the praise.

That afternoon a piece of paper stating that Private Patrick J. McGurk respectfully begged to submit his application for a change of religion from Roman Catholic to atheist and affirming that the said private respectfully remained the commanding officer's most obedient servant, was handed, for submission through the proper channels, to Company Sergeant Squad O'Rourke.

A short time later Squad came roaring into the orderly room and wanted to know the meaning of this nonsense, at which he waved the application under the Slater's nose.

"I've lost the faith," the Slater said calmly.

"Lost the faith!" Squad bellowed. "You don't like the way the Man Upstairs is handling things, I suppose?"

"I don't think there *is* any Man Upstairs," said the Slater.

For once in his life Squad was thunderstruck. He stormed into the adjutant's office and laid the application in front of Pettigo. "Sir," he said, his voice quivering with outrage, "we've a bloody mutiny on our hands."

Five minutes later the Slater was called into the office. Pettigo looked up from his desk and asked, "What's the meaning of this?"

"Please, sir, I've lost the faith."

"Ah ha, very good. I'm sure this will throw the heavens into confusion." Percy's dark eyes squinted meanly. "What am I supposed to do with it?" He tapped the piece of paper with his finger.

"Please, sir, I want to be listed on my army records as an atheist."

"I see. And you expect to get taken off the parade for the rest of the mission?"

The Slater pondered the question for several seconds, as though the thought had just occurred to him. "Yes, sir. If I'm detailed for the parade I'll have to write to the army solicitor general saying that I'm forced to worship in a faith that I don't belong to."

"Oh, McGurk, you're a cute one. This, I presume, is the result of the detail I gave you this morning." His voice was low and conversational but the Slater wasn't fooled.

"Oh, no, sir! It was coming back from the mess hall that I lost the faith."

"I see. A great revelation, no doubt, accompanied by flashes of light and peals of thunder?"

"Nothing as grand as that, sir," the Slater answered modestly. "Just a quiet wee revelation you might say."

"By Jingo, there'll be more quiet revelations in store for you before this is over," the adjutant threatened, his voice rising. With an effort he changed tactics and managed to say, almost kindly, "Now listen, McGurk. Let's have an end to this nonsense. We'll forget about taking names if you'll pass the word that I want nobody walking out until the sermon is over."

"I'll do that for you, sir, but I think you should have the company sergeant make that announcement. It would hardly do for a private to be telling the men how to conduct themselves."

The adjutant's hand descended on the paper with a bang. "Listen to me. I want you on that parade, and you'll stand at the church door and take the name of anyone who leaves.

That isn't forcing you to do anything against this new religion of yours. Is that perfectly clear?"

"Yes, sir. Which door shall I stand at, sir? There's four of them," the Slater asked innocently.

"Stand at the main door!" the adjutant shouted, half rising from the chair.

"Is that all, sir?"

"Yes! Now clear out of here!"

The Slater went back to his work in the orderly room. He was in the middle of typing the following day's Daily Ration Report when Percy came out of his office in a series of spasmodic jerks. "You're to report immediately to the C.O.," he ordered with a glare.

"Very good, sir." The Slater put on his cap, left the orderly room, and reported to the C.O.'s office. He opened the door, threw a snappy salute, and said, "Private McGurk reporting, sir."

The C.O. looked up from the gun catalogue he was reading and frowned. "Yes. Yes, *McGurk*." He tried to connect the name with some information his mind was trying to recall. Although a scant twenty minutes had passed since the adjutant had phoned with a request that he talk to the Slater, the C.O. had already forgotten the conversation. "Well, now, what's all this about?" he said in an attempt to uncover the Slater's mission.

The Slater smiled and said helpfully, "Please, sir, I want to change my religion."

Remembrance came flooding back to the C.O. "Won't do at all. What is it, McGurk?"

"What is what, sir?"

"What's behind this change of religion? You trying to get a discharge, isn't that it?"

"Oh, no, sir! I've lost the faith."

The C.O. groaned in despair. With one thing and another, he seemed to be having an inordinate amount of trouble with this McGurk. If it wasn't a discharge, then it must be the other thing. "Do you know what *your* problem is?" he shot out suddenly.

"No, sir," the Slater dutifully replied.

Webley lowered his voice to a hoarse whisper. "Women!"

"Women, sir?"

"Women," Webley affirmed. "What you need is a woman. Why don't you find a nice lassie and get married? I wasn't worth a tinker's dam until I married. Best thing in the world for a soldier." The C.O. leaned back in his chair and gave the ceiling a smug look. "When I first met my wife, I was a second lieutenant. Now I'm a commandant," he said with an air of simple wisdom.

"Very good, sir," the Slater approved.

"Do you have a girl?"

The Slater blushed. "No, sir."

"Then get one and marry her. If you can't get married, at least find a bad girl somewhere to take your mind off things."

"Yes, sir."

"Now like a good man, you'll withdraw that application?"

"No, sir."

"Ah, you're a difficult man," the C.O. said with sudden conviction. He hunched forward over the desk and fixed the Slater with a bewitching wall-eyed stare. "Why don't you take a week's annual leave and think it over? When you come back we might forget about putting the leave down in your records. Find a girl at home and get married. What do you think of that now?" The C.O. leaned back with the air of a man who has just played his ace of trumps.

For a moment the Slater was tempted by the bribe, but his resolve was stiffened by the thought of his friends who were depending on him. "I'm sorry, sir. I can't withdraw the application."

"You're going to be thick about this?"

"Yes, sir."

"Right then. I'll forward the application to command, but I doubt if you'll get a discharge." It was either a discharge or women, and the Slater seemed too innocent to be really bothered by women. "You may go now," he said unmilitarily.

The Slater was no sooner settled at his work than the adjutant was out to him again. "Well now, McGurk, did you nail your thesis to the C.O.'s door?"

"Beg pardon, sir?"

"Never mind. I've been talking to the C.O., and we've agreed that you should see the post chaplain before we send the application through to command."

"Sir, I wouldn't think of putting anyone to trouble over me," the Slater objected.

"It's no trouble," the adjutant said with a sickening smile. "Isn't that what the chaplain's for? To help us with these problems of faith and morals?"

"Yes, sir."

"Father Moran's waiting for you."

"Very good, sir." The Slater let his lip curl about one-hundredth of an inch. The sneer came and went so quickly that Percy wondered if his imagination was playing tricks. He retaliated with a fierce Prussian glare.

The Slater squared his shoulders, saluted, and left the orderly room. As he reluctantly made his way to the post chaplain's office, he marshaled his arguments and found them rather thin. He didn't mind facing the adjutant or the C.O., but Father Moran was a different kettle of fish. There was something about the clergy that frightened the Slater.

"*There* you are," Father Moran said as he rose from his chair, the light of battle in his eyes. Although the chaplain specialized in great sinners, it wasn't every day that an atheist came along. "Sit down!" he boomed in a bloodthirsty tone. The Slater perched timidly on the edge of an armchair.

Father Moran leaped from behind his desk and strode over to the window. He turned his back on the sinner and remained silent for a long minute, a technique that he had found to be very effective. "What's this I hear about you losing . . . the . . . faith?" The words rolled out in funeral-march tempo.

"It's true, Father." The Slater squirmed backward into the chair.

The priest turned around from the window. "Just what do you no longer believe in?"

The Slater straightened with a jerk. "The whole shooting gallery," he answered in a rush. "I don't believe in the Apostles' Creed, nor the Immaculate Conception, nor the Holy Ghost, nor Blessed Oliver Plunkett, nor the Children of Mary."

The priest held up his hand, a pained look on his face. "Enough! God save us, do you want the earth to open and swallow us all?"

The Slater looked down at the wooden floor.

"We'll step softly around the Holy Ghost," the priest said. He pulled over a stool and sat close to the Slater. His voice was low and earnest. "Exactly when was it that you started doubting?"

"It was the year Kerry lost the All-Ireland final, Father," the Slater rapidly improvised.

"What had that to do with it?"

"Kerry had a priest playing on their side, Father. The left full forward was a newly ordained Dominican."

"Ah, my son." Father Moran sighed, appalled at the Slater's ignorance. "And do you think that God, with all the troubles and evil that does be plaguing the world, has time to see that Kerry wins an old football game?"

"It seemed odd at the time," the Slater answered defensively.

The priest jumped up and returned to the window, clasping his hands behind his back. "Girls?" he boomed, rocking back on his heels.

"Father?"

"Girls! Do you go out with girls?" The priest's tone was impatient, as though vexed that the Slater had made him spell it out.

"Sometimes."

"Impure actions?"

"No, Father. Not the girls I know," the Slater said sadly.

"Impure thoughts?"

The Slater hesitated. "Sometimes when I go to bed at night, Father."

"A prayer to the Blessed Virgin," Father Moran said in the manner of a doctor prescribing a pill for a commonplace ailment. He came back to the Slater and stared down at him with a holy concentration. His voice took on a throbbing undertone. "Pray! Prayer is our greatest weapon against the devil and his works. Pray against the evil that blackens our hearts with sin. Pray to the Blessed Virgin to guard over our senses." The priest closed his eyes and raised his face to the ceiling.

The Slater uncomfortably wondered if Father Moran had gone into a trance. He waited a minute and then coughed apologetically. "Yes, Father."

The priest looked down and his mood changed to one of brisk efficiency. "Now remember, watch the impure thoughts and actions and keep away from dirty women. Pray to St. Thomas Aquinas for faith and to the Blessed Virgin to guard you against evil thoughts. Will you do that now?" He grasped the Slater by the arm.

"Yes, Father." The Slater winced at the tightness of the grip.

"Very good. God bless you, my son," Father Moran said, ushering the bewildered Slater out the door.

Back in the orderly room, Lieutenant Pettigo had been busy. He had originally intended to harry the Slater with interviews and inquisitions until the victim gave in through pure fatigue. But like a good general, Percy had developed alternate plans, one of which he was sure would succeed. He awaited the Slater's return with a Machiavellian calm.

The Slater sloped in the door of the orderly room and went quietly back to his work. Quiet as he was, the adjutant heard him. He came out of his office and said, "Back from the Council of Leipzig?"

"Sir?" The Slater smiled painfully.

"Do you still want the application forwarded?"

"Yes, sir."

"Good." The adjutant gave a crooked smile. "You know that we'll have to write a letter to your next of kin informing them of your change of religion? According to regulations, when there's a change in a soldier's vital statistics his next of kin have to be notified."

The Slater closed his eyes and vividly imagined the incredulous shock on his mother's face when she read that he had abandoned the faith. He saw her in sackcloth and ashes, adding an extra decade to the evening rosary for the return of the lost one. He saw her tearfully barraging St. Anne with novenas. But worst of all, he knew that she would unmercifully castigate herself for having reared a son who had fallen away from the Church. He voiced his objection, "Sir, I don't think that's necessary. I'd rather explain it to her myself."

The adjutant saw the worried fear in the Slater's eyes. Positive now of his strategic strength, he pressed the attack.

"The regulations state an official notification, which means a letter from the commanding officer."

"Sir," the Slater appealed. "Perhaps I'd better not change, after all. Father Moran said if I prayed I might get back the faith, and maybe I should wait a few weeks before I change—to see if the faith comes back," he finished weakly.

The adjutant set the point of his lance at the Slater's throat. "While you're waiting I think you should listen carefully to the sermon each night. I'm sure the missioners will help you to reach the right conclusion."

"Very good, sir."

Merciless, the adjutant sent the lance home. "If you see any ordnance men leaving the church, I want you to take their names."

The Slater only offered token resistance. "Is that an order, sir?" he feebly asked.

Percy smiled and left the office without replying. He knew that no one would leave the church.

For the rest of the mission the Knave kept desperately trying to find another loophole. Finally, however, he and the Slater conceded that battle to the company adjutant.

Frank O'Connor

THE FIRST CONFESSION

It was a Saturday afternoon in early spring. A small boy whose face looked as though it had been but newly scrubbed was being led by the hand by his sister through a crowded street. The little boy showed a marked reluctance to proceed; he affected to be very interested in the shop windows. Equally, his sister seemed to pay no attention to them. She tried to hurry him; he resisted. When she dragged him he began to bawl. The hatred with which she viewed him was almost diabolical, but when she spoke her words and tone were full of passionate sympathy.

"Ah, sha, God help us!" she intoned into his ear in a whine of commiseration.

"Leave me go!" he said, digging his heels into the pavement. "I don't want to go. I want to go home."

"But, sure, you can't go home, Jackie. You'll have to go. The parish priest will be up to the house with a stick."

"I don't care. I won't go."

"Oh, Sacred Heart, isn't it a terrible pity you weren't a good boy? Oh, Jackie, me heart bleeds for you! I don't know what they'll do to you at all, Jackie, me poor child. And all the trouble you caused your poor old Nanny, and the way you wouldn't eat in the same room with her, and the time you kicked her on the shins, and the time you went for me with the bread knife under the table. I don't know will he ever listen to you at all, Jackie. I think meself he might send you to the Bishop. Oh, Jackie, how will you think of all your sins?"

Half stupefied with terror, Jackie allowed himself to be led through the sunny streets to the very gates of the church. It was an old one with two grim iron gates and a long, low, shapeless stone front. At the gates he stuck, but it was already too late. She dragged him behind her across the yard, and the commiserating whine with which she had tried to madden him gave place to a yelp of triumph.

"Now you're caught! And I hope he'll give you the pinitintial psalms! That'll cure you, you suppurating little caffler!"

Jackie gave himself up for lost. Within the old church there was no stained glass; it was cold and dark and desolate, and in the silence the trees in the yard knocked hollowly at the tall windows. He allowed himself to be led through the vaulted silence, the intense and magical silence which seemed to have frozen within the ancient walls, buttressing them and shouldering the high wooden roof. In the street outside, yet seeming a million miles away, a ballad singer was drawling a ballad.

Nora sat in front of him beside the confession box. There were a few old women before her, and later a thin, sad-looking man with long hair came and sat beside Jackie. In the intense silence of the church that seemed to grow deeper from the plaintive moaning of the ballad singer, he could hear the buzz-buzz of a woman's voice in the box, and then the husky ba-ba-ba of the priest's. Lastly the soft thud of something that signalled the end of the confession, and out came the woman, head lowered, hands joined, looking neither to right nor left, and tiptoed up to the altar to say her penance.

It seemed only a matter of seconds till Nora rose and with a whispered injunction disappeared from his sight. He was all alone. Alone and next to be heard and the fear of damnation in his soul. He looked at the sad-faced man. He was gazing at the roof, his hands joined in prayer. A woman in a red blouse and black shawl had taken her place below him. She uncovered her head, fluffed her hair out roughly with her hand, brushed it sharply back, then, bowing, caught it in a knot, and pinned it on her neck. Nora emerged. Jackie rose and looked at her with a hatred which was inappropriate to the occasion and the place. Her hands were joined on her stomach, her eyes modestly lowered, and her face had an expression of the most rapt and tender recollection. With death in his heart he crept into the compartment she left open and drew the door shut behind him.

He was in pitch darkness. He could see no priest or anything else. And anything he had heard of confession got all muddled up in his mind. He knelt to the right-hand wall and said: "Bless me, Father, for I have sinned. This is my first confession." Nothing happened. He repeated it louder. Still it gave no answer. He turned to the opposite wall, genuflected first, then again went on his knees and repeated the charm. This time he was certain he would receive a reply, but none came. He repeated the process with the remaining wall without effect. He had the feeling of someone with an unfamiliar machine, of pressing buttons at random. And finally the thought struck him that God knew. God knew about the bad confession he intended to make and had made him deaf and blind so that he could neither hear nor see the priest.

Then as his eyes grew accustomed to the blackness, he perceived something he had not noticed previously: a sort of a shelf at about the height of his head. The purpose of this eluded him for a moment. Then he understood. It was for kneeling on.

He had always prided himself upon his powers of climbing, but this took it out of him. There was no foothold. He slipped twice before he succeeded in getting his knee on it, and the strain of drawing the rest of his body up was almost more than he was capable of. However, he did at last get his two knees on it, there was just room for those, but his legs hung down uncomfortably and the edge of the shelf bruised his shins. He joined his hands and pressed the last remaining button. "Bless me, Father, for I have sinned. This is my first confession."

At the same moment the slide was pushed back and a dim light streamed into the little box. There was an uncomfortable silence, and then an alarmed voice asked, "Who's there?" Jackie found it almost impossible to speak into the grille which was on a level with his knees, but he got a firm grip of the molding above it, bent his head down and sideways, and as though he were hanging by his feet like a monkey, found himself looking almost upside down at the priest. But the priest was looking sideways at him, and Jackie, whose knees were being tortured by this new position, felt it was a queer way to hear confessions.

"'Tis me, Father," he piped, and then, running all his words together in excitement, he rattled off, "Bless me, Father, for I have sinned. This is my first confession."

"What?" exclaimed a deep and angry voice, and the sombre soutaned figure stood bolt upright, disappearing almost entirely from Jackie's view. "What does this mean? What are you doing there? Who are you?" And with the shock, Jackie felt his hands lose their grip and his legs their balance. He discovered himself tumbling into space, and falling, he knocked his head against the door, which shot open and permitted him to thump right into the centre of the aisle. Straight on this came a small, dark-haired priest with a biretta well forward on his head. At the same time Nora came skeltering madly down the church.

"Lord God!" she cried. "The snivelling little caffler! I knew he'd do it! I knew he'd disgrace me!"

Jackie received a clout over the ear which reminded him that for some strange reason he had not yet begun to cry and that people might possibly think he wasn't hurt at all. Nora slapped him again.

"What's this? What's this?" cried the priest. "Don't attempt to beat the child, you little vixen!"

"I can't do me pinance with him," cried Nora shrilly, cocking a shocked eye on the priest. "He had me driven mad. Stop your crying, you dirty scut! Stop it now or I'll make you cur at the other side of your ugly puss!"

"Run away out of this, you little jade!" growled the priest. He suddenly began to laugh, took out a pocket handkerchief, and wiped Jackie's nose. "You're not hurt, sure you're not. Show us the ould head. . . . Ah, 'tis nothing. 'Twill be better before you're twice married. . . . So you were coming to confession?"

"I was, Father."

"A big fellow like you should have terrible sins. Is it your first?"

" 'Tis, Father."

"Oh, my, worse and worse! Here, sit down there and wait till I get rid of these ould ones and we'll have a long chat. Never mind that sister of yours."

With a feeling of importance that glowed through his tears Jackie waited. Nora stuck out her tongue at him, but he didn't even bother to reply. A great feeling of relief was welling up in him. The sense of oppression that had been weighing him down for a week, the knowledge that he was about to make a bad confession, disappeared. Bad confession, indeed! He had made friends, made friends with the priest, and the priest expected, even demanded, terrible sins. Oh, women! It was all women and girls and their silly talk. They had no real knowledge of the world!

And when the time came for him to make his confession he did not beat about the bush. He may have clenched his hands and lowered his eyes, but wouldn't anyone?

"Father," he said huskily, "I made it up to kill me grandmother."

There was a moment's pause. Jackie did not dare to look up, but he could feel the priest's eyes on him. The priest's voice also seemed a trifle husky.

"Your grandmother?" he asked, but he didn't after all sound very angry.

"Yes, Father."

"And why did you want to kill her?"

"Oh, God, Father, she's a horrible woman!"

"Is she now?"

"She is, Father."

"What way is she horrible?"

Jackie paused to think. It was hard to explain.

"She takes snuff, Father."

"Oh, my!"

"And she goes round in her bare feet, Father."

"Tut-tut-tut!"

"She's a horrible woman, Father," said Jackie with sudden earnestness. "She takes porter. And she ates the potatoes off the table with her hands. And me mother do be out working most days, and since that one came 'tis she gives us our dinner and I can't ate the dinner." He found himself sniffling. "And she gives pinnies to Nora and she doesn't give no pinnies to me because she knows I can't stand her. And me father sides with her, Father, and he hates me, and me heart is broken and wan night in bed I made it up the way I'd kill her."

Jackie began to sob again, rubbing his nose with his sleeve, as he remembered his wrongs.

"And what way were you going to kill her?" asked the priest smoothly.

"With a hatchet, Father."

"When she was in bed?"

"No, Father."

"How, so?"

"When she ates the potatoes and drinks the porter she falls asleep, Father."

"And you'd hit her then?"

"Yes, Father."

"Wouldn't a knife be better?"

"'Twould, Father, only I'd be afraid of the blood."

"Oh, of course. I never thought of the blood."

"I'd be afraid of that, Father. I near hit Nora with the bread knife one time she came after me under the table, only I was afraid."

"You're a terrible child," said the priest with awe.

"I am, Father," said Jackie noncommittally, sniffling back his tears.

"And what would you do with the body?"

"How, Father?"

"Wouldn't someone see her and tell?"

"I was going to cut her up with a knife and take away the pieces and bury them. I could get an orange box for three pence and make a cart to take them away."

"My, my," said the priest. "You had it all well planned."

"Ah, I tried that," said Jackie with mounting confidence. "I borrowed a cart and practised it by meself one night after dark."

"And you weren't afraid?"

"Ah, no," said Jackie halfheartedly. "Only a bit."

"You have terrible courage," said the priest. "There's a lot of people I want to get rid of, but I'm not like you. I'd never have the courage. And hanging is an awful death."

"Is it?" asked Jackie, responding to the brightness of a new theme.

"Oh, an awful blooming death!"

"Did you ever see a fellow hanged?"

"Dozens of them, and they all died roaring."

"Jay!" said Jackie.

"They do be swinging out of them for hours and the poor fellows lepping and roaring, like bells in a belfry, and then they put lime on them to burn them up. Of course, they pretend they're dead, but sure, they don't be dead at all."

"Jay!" said Jackie again.

"So if I were you I'd take my time and think about it. In my opinion 'tisn't worth it, not even to get rid of a grandmother. I asked dozens of fellows like you that killed their grandmothers about it, and they all said, 'No, 'twasn't worth it.' . . ."

Nora was waiting in the yard. The sunlight struck down on her across the high wall and its brightness made his eyes dazzle. "Well?" she asked. "What did he give you?"

"Three Hail Marys."

"You mustn't have told him anything."

"I told him everything," said Jackie confidently.

"What did you tell him?"

"Things you don't know."

"Bah! He gave you three Hail Marys because you were a crybaby!"

Jackie didn't mind. He felt the world was very good. He began to whistle as well as the hindrance in his jaw permitted.

"What are you sucking?"

"Bull's-eyes."

"Was it he gave them to you?"

" 'Twas."

"Almighty God!" said Nora. "Some people have all the luck. I might as well be a sinner like you. There's no use in being good."

Frank Leslie

THERE'S A SPOT IN MY HEART

Uncle George described himself as one of the "Church Militant" and said that Grandfather was "anticlerical." Both terms were rather loosely categorical. My grandfather was hardly "anti" anything—he seldom gave a damn—while "Militant" was too fragile a word to define Uncle George's emotions on the Church. "Church Rampant" might have been more accurate, although "Church Berserk" was even closer to it.

My grandfather, like a lot of people who find living an all-sufficient and engrossing pursuit, affected a temperate skepticism regarding spiritual matters. It was not that he disbelieved in God, but he distrusted most allegations concerning His methods. Where conditions are imposed upon conduct—particularly with such appalling sanctions—my grandfather thought that the involuntary subjects of the law have an elementary right to ask for explicit terms. They should not be forced to construction and conjecture on evidence that was, at best, highly circumstantial. There was a duty on the lawmaker to promulgate the law, and the dictates of Omnipotence, if they were valid, could be expected to have, at least, the measure of publication that we were accustomed to find in a municipal ordinance on the regulation of street peddlers.

My grandfather believed that the principles of conduct followed from the natural order of things—like the "House Rules" in a gentleman's club, they were obvious or implicit, and whatever modifications were necessary to conform to local custom or conditions could be adequately taken care of by the "House Committee," who were your friends, associates, and fellow members. He also felt that good behavior was as personal a matter as a hot bath, and people should not expect reward or praise for it, any more than they should expect to be complimented for not stinking.

There was no little irony in the fact that my grandfather was quite popular with the priests who visited our house, while they shied from Uncle George as though he were one of the more lethal of the Seven Deadly Sins. My grandfather had a charm of manner and was always the soul of gracious hospitality. He offered the clergy a cigar, a drink, and a safe topic of conversation, and there are few priests who will decline them all. Uncle George, on the other hand, tested them for their orthodoxy and gave them oral examinations in canon law and liturgy.

My grandfather was a man who took no one's assumptions at face value. He believed that an office—even a sacred office—conferred nothing gratuitous in the way of human merit. You could be a priest and a gentleman—and most generally you were—according to my grandfather; but you could be a priest and an ass, too, and when you were, there was no Roman collar high enough to hide your ears.

Uncle George, who was compounded, spiritually, in eccentric proportions, of Savonarola, Saint Jude, and Father Dooley's bitch, accused Grandfather of lacking "respect for the cloth." My grandfather said that he had the highest respect for the cloth; he merely did not like to see it being used to wrap up a fool.

("Talking about priests!" exclaimed my grandmother in horror. "There will be no luck in this house!"

("Perhaps not," replied my grandfather quietly, "and there will be no Tinhorn Torquemadas, either," he added, looking straight at Uncle George.)

The presence under the same roof of two persons who held such diverse opinions on almost every subject would seem, more or less inevitably, to lead to many heated disputes upon the most controversial subject of all. Yet the question of religion was the incredible exception. There were, occasionally, short, sharp exchanges at point-blank range between my grandfather and Uncle George on matters that might be said to have, incidentally, a religious aspect, but there were never religious arguments, as such, in the usual logomachical sense.

Had there been any real argument, Uncle George would have easily carried off the honors. He had Truth, Revelation, and Theology on his side. Had anything ever been proved, he would have proved it. His reasoning was valid and his procedure soundly dialectical. He could have demonstrated or controverted as the situation required. Uncle George was stalwart in the Faith, and he fought upstanding, as befits a true soldier of the Church.

My grandfather's methods were strictly partisan. He crept past the sentries and knifed an argument. He lay patiently in ambush to derail a train of thought. His main objectives were confusion and diversion. He never engaged a front or exposed a flank. His tactics were guerrilla; his weapon, the needle.

Some of my grandfather's best opportunities came when he was attempting—in the exercise of common hospitality—to draw off Uncle George from the badgering of some unfortunate priest who happened to be a guest in our house. For Uncle George was more Catholic than the Church, and his favorite sport was priest-baiting. There were a thousand odds and ends of theology, canon law, and episcopal jurisdiction which rattled around inside his head, and you never knew what combination he was going to throw out next.

My grandfather's commando sallies in defense of the courtesy and honor of our house were not infrequently effective by way of raising a counterembarrassment, for he was addicted to a sort of crisp humor which often had a trace of the bawdy in it. The clerical guest was sometimes racked between the irresistible impulse to guffaw—as a relief from tension—and the immovable dignity of his official position.

I recall the minor incident of the Reverend Father Gerald McManus, curate, who came to our house in the exercise of his priestly duty of visiting the sick during an illness of my grandmother's. Father McManus was an extremely shy young man, and the oil of ordination still glistened upon him. He was serious and full of zeal and most anxious to resolve the rational difficulties of the laity wherever he found them.

An acute scarcity of satisfying difficulties among the laity was perhaps the solitary disappointment he had found in Holy Orders. For he believed that a more than modest competency in Sacred Theology and a better than average comprehension of the *Summa* deserved a broader field than the small limitations of the young ladies' sodality. How would Augustine or Aquinas have replied to such persistent queries as, "Father, is it a sin to chew gum?" or, "Father, can I marry a divorced atheist whose ex-wife is living, if he is willing to be baptized a Catholic?" How, indeed! Father McManus sometimes wondered as he dreamed of disputations with Melanchthon.

He had learned many things in the seminary, practical as well as doctrinal, and he felt amply prepared to meet all comers. That there might be a chink in the armor they had girded on his loins, he could not conceive. But, alas, there was. For somehow they had neglected to teach him how to deal with a member of his own flock who backed him into a corner and made implied accusations of laxity and heresy.

Unwarily, he accepted Uncle George's invitation to sit in the parlor, and hardly had he settled himself in the chair when Uncle George moved in with one of his favorite openings: the magnificence of plain chant versus the odious and uncanonical caterwauling of mixed choirs. Father McManus, made softer than he knew by training on the cardboard pushovers which the Children of Mary set up for him, attempted a facetious feint. He never quite realized what hit him when Uncle George swarmed all over him with decrees of the Council of Trent, more recent regulations of the Sacred Congregation of Rites, and direct citations from a bull of John XXII. Before he could regain his balance he was parrying an interrogation on the nature of Sanctifying Grace and, having countered with a Dominican defense, found himself buried under an avalanche of Jesuitisms. After a further incautious lead, he was hanging on the ropes, desperately endeavoring to duck a haymaker of the heresy of Jansenism which Uncle George was trying to land.

When my grandfather appeared on the scene from behind the portieres, Uncle George, holding forth on the abysmal failure of the modern clergy to inspire the faithful, was swinging into a rousing windup.

"Without a vigorous priesthood we cannot have a militant Christianity," he declaimed to the now helpless and bewildered curate. "Why are there no Christian martyrs in our times? Why are we Christians poorer in spirit than mere Mohammedans? Yes, Mohammedans! Did you ever consider this fact—that Christ offered the world the Beatific Vision-solace from spiritual doubt—realization for all the capacities of the higher faculties—while Mohammed gave the world a seven-storied brothel—a towering palace of carnalities—a promise of an apotheosis of lewdity! And what do we find? We find those who profess Christ indifferent and slothful, wavering and watery in the practice and belief of their Holy Religion, while Mohammed's millions are still charging into the teeth of the Unbelievers' guns, greedy for that martyrdom whose recompense is lust! To think that we, who hold ourselves as Christians—"

"I wouldn't be so hard on the Christians, George," said my grandfather suddenly from the doorway. "After all, a Mohammedan can anticipate while a Christian can only hope."

The next time my grandmother got sick they sent the pastor.

Eric Cross

THE POWERS OF IMAGINATION

"You'll remember to give a sop of hay to the cow," said Michael Sullivan, as he drew on his coat.

"Indeed, but I'm less likely to forget that," replied his wife, "than you are to remember the bottle of water from St. Brigid's well that I've been asking you to get for me for months past."

"Yerra, woman, I'm going on business—not to be traipsing bottles of spring water about the countryside like a mineral-water manufacturer. We've water enough in the well at the door, and as for the rest of it, 'tis all in the power of imagination, as I've told you a hundred times."

"Imagination or no imagination, 'twould be better for you than to be traipsing bottles of poteen round the countryside till one day the guards catch you. 'Tis then you'll want the imagination to pay the fine."

"Guards—where are you? To hear the way you talk, anyone would think it was only yesterday I was born. I'd best be off or I'll miss the train."

He started up the track, over the shoulder of the hill. The bottle of poteen in his overcoat pocket bumped heavily against his thigh as he walked. It was a pleasant bumping, however, he mused, as soon it would be salved by the pound note he would get from Dick Hegarty for it. Yes, a pound at least. "A bottle of the best," was the message, "for a man who wants it for greyhounds and won't be mean about the price asked. If he's satisfied there will be further orders. A strong buyer, now, so don't be letting me down and letting yourself down into the bargain."

A pound a bottle and further orders, Michael Sullivan reflected. And that might mean, say a bottle a day. And there were six days in the week, forgetting Sunday, when most likely he'd have no need for it for greyhounds. Six days a week at a pound a day. That would be six pounds a week . . . that was a deal better than even ganger's job with the county council. Six pounds a week . . . and say, fifty working weeks in the year . . . that would be three hundred pounds a year. Three hundred pounds a year! What chance had a man to earn that slaving from morning to night, winter and summer, on a mountainy farm? It was every bit as good as a sergeant's job in the guards. And to think of herself bothering him about an ould bottle of well water when he was almost in the way of being set up as a businessman. Women were queer . . . they had the bad word for everything and no right use of their imagination at all.

The Kilbrigid train was already in and waiting for the branch-line connection when he reached the station. He took his seat in an empty compartment and cut himself a fill of tobacco and stretched at his ease. Then the foxy-haired fellow came in. He had always a dislike of a foxy man. Somehow they always seemed to spell trouble. The foxy man passed the time of day. Michael packed his pipe, and threw open his coat for the matches in his inner pocket before he remembered. But it was too late. The foxy-haired fellow's eyes had spotted the bottle.

"A drop of the right stuff, I suppose," he said, sliding over on the seat. "I hear they have a great reputation for the making of it hereabouts."

But Michael Sullivan was much too quick for him.

" 'Tis only a bottle of blessed water I'm taking in to a sick relation," he replied, without hesitation.

"Sure—of course it is," replied the foxy man. "Now what would be the price of a right bottle of it?" he continued.

" 'Tis a bottle of blessed water, I'm telling you."

"Manalive, we're agreed on that. 'Tis the matter of the price and the quality I'm interested in."

At that moment, however, the branch-line train pulled in

and the foxy-haired man's attention was diverted. He spotted someone he was apparently waiting for down the platform and got hurriedly out of the compartment, and Michael Sullivan was greatly relieved at his going. After all he could be, as likely as not, a guard or detective in plain clothes, for there was a court in Kilbrigid that day. If only the train would start.

But the momentary relief was cut from its roots when, as the train was on the point of starting, the foxy-haired man jumped into the compartment, this time with two guards, confirming Michael Sullivan's apprehension.

However, they took little notice of him beyond a curt nod to him—or so it seemed. But that was small consolation to him. From somewhere at the back of his mind there came the remembrance that you couldn't be arrested on a moving train. That was why they said nothing and did nothing. They were waiting till he stepped out onto the platform at Kilbrigid. Then they would surround him and arrest him, search his pockets, and find the evidence on him.

It all came of herself putting the bad word on the start of his journey. Now she would have the laugh on him, but the dear laugh. It might be a lesson to her if nothing else, and teach her not to be drawing down misfortune with her tongue.

The group had got into an argument between themselves in the meantime. They were disputing the rights and the wrongs of a case to be heard that day, and it was plain enough from the talk that the foxy-haired man was a detective, all right.

"I tell you that he'll get off on a point of law," asserted the detective.

"You're letting your imagination run away with you, young fellow me lad. 'Tis a good thing that you have the guards to protect you from your ignorance," laughed one of the others, who had the stripes of a sergeant. "The law's a trickier thing than you think."

"Will you bet a level pound on it then?" whipped back the detective.

"I will, I will," replied the sergeant eagerly. " 'Twill be the easiest money I ever won."

The matter did not concern Michael Sullivan. He had enough to worry him, but he could not help hearing it. The words and phrases floated into his mind, mingling with his brooding. "A point of the law . . . The law's a trickier thing . . ." Then, suddenly, the ghost of a smile came to his face as an idea blossomed. Guards, where are you? He wasn't born yesterday. The laugh was with him now. Where were they at all? Ah, they had just passed Mauleen. A couple of miles and they would be coming to the Gorey tunnel . . . the creamery . . . Pat Lucey's cross . . . the main road . . . any moment now.

Suddenly the train plunged into darkness. Sulphurous smoke belched and billowed into the compartment through the wide-open window. Quick as a cat he jumped up, whipped the bottle from his pocket, and dropped it out, and then noisily pulled up the window. When the train came out into the daylight again he was sitting in his corner, quietly smiling to himself. Guards, where are you?

He waited in joyful contemplation of the moment when they had stopped in Kilbrigid and the train had emptied and he was walking away about his business and the sergeant came alongside him and put his hand on his shoulder. Then he would have the laugh on them. But, more than that, he would have the law on them. He would show them that they could not do what they liked with Michael Sullivan.

He would let them take him to the barracks through the streets of Kilbrigid. There he would ask for a solicitor. Old Gerahty would be his man. He would claim compensation for unlawful arrest and public loss of character without a shred of evidence against him. He knew the law all right, and these fellows could not do just as they liked with law-abiding men. The smile on his face broadened. He had been anticipating a miserable pound for the day. Why, this day would be worth hundreds at least. Michael Sullivan wasn't born yesterday.

The train drew into Kilbrigid. The sergeant and guard leaped out. Sullivan took his time, drawing his coat round him and buttoning it slowly. He stepped out onto the platform.

The foxy-haired detective followed him out. How clever they were—or thought they were with their plan. Just too clever by half. The moment was approaching which would be great re-telling through the winter months.

The detective sidled up to him and walked alongside him.

"If it's the right stuff I'll give you fifteen bob for it."

"I don't know what you are talking about," replied Sullivan with great dignity.

"Yerra, man, stop your codding. I've greyhounds myself. I'll make it seventeen-and-six, and you can hand it over to me in the waiting room."

"'Tis a bottle of blessed water, I'm after telling you before."

"All right, all right. Have it your own way. You're a hard man. I'll go to an even pound."

The sergeant and the guard were waiting ahead for him. "Come on, Mich," they called impatiently, "we're late enough already."

The detective drew away. "You'll do no better than that. They are a mean lot in Kilbrigid. An even pound. I'll see you on the five-o'clock train."

Guards and detective disappeared into the street, and Michael Sullivan was left alone with his empty victory. All that he had done was to make a fool, a double fool, of himself. Here he was in Kilbrigid with the whole day wasted before him, empty of purpose, devoid of profit, just because he had let his imagination run away with him.

He dared not show his face into Hegarty's now unless he wanted dog's abuse. He wandered round the town looking into the shopwindows. He had a pint and a bite to eat in a pub. He walked out one road and then another in order to fill the empty mocking hours. He had another drink and got an empty wine bottle from the barman and then went along to St. Brigid's well outside the town and filled it. He might as well be doing that as anything. At least he would not have to listen to herself nagging him about that when he got back; small consolation though that would be.

He took his seat in the return train early. As five o'clock approached it began to fill. The sergeant and guard got into the compartment but beyond a nod, paid no attention to him. Just before the train started the detective came bustling along, looking for them, and came breezily in.

"Come along, sergeant, pay up and look smiling. You can't pull wool over the eyes of the detective force you know."

"All right, all right, me boy. There's your pound for you. But don't let it go to your head. 'Tis but beginner's luck—and you'll probably pay dearly for it."

The detective took the pound and kissed it in triumph. The train started, and after a few moments he slid over to Michael Sullivan. Nodding toward the bulge in his overcoat pocket, he said, "I see you didn't do your bit of business. I told you that they were a mean lot in Kilbrigid. But I won't go back on my offer. A pound and it's a deal."

Michael Sullivan wasn't in the mood for reviving the subject with all its bitter personal recriminations, and answered him snappishly.

"I'm telling you that it's a bottle of blessed water. The relation was taken away to the hospital and I was too late." But even as he said the words, almost mechanically, there was a stirring in his mind. It wasn't quite clear yet, but some sort of an idea was being born.

"Well—they're tough, mighty tough in the West. Come on, man, make it a deal for twenty-two-and-six."

Michael Sullivan held his peace. He was letting the idea dry its wings.

"All right—'tis as you say. 'Tis a bottle of blessed water, and I'm paying twenty-two-and-six for it. Now will that do you? I'll pay you over the money now and you can leave the bottle on the seat when you get out."

The idea was taking form, though it was not yet quite distinct. "I wouldn't have it on my conscience to be swindling any man or to be selling him a thing under false pretenses. 'Tis but a bottle of blessed water. Let the sergeant there judge."

With that he drew the bottle from his pocket and handed it to the sergeant. The sergeant scanned it carefully. He drew the cork and smelled the contents of the bottle with leisurely deliberation. He put the bottle to his lips and tasted it, rolling it round his mouth. Then he smacked his lips, rammed the cork back tightly into the bottle, and handed it back to Sullivan.

" 'Tis the true, genuine and unadulterated article—and well I should know it, being brought up on it almost, as you might say. Time and time again it has saved my life. 'Tis a certain cure for rheumatism, sciaticy, and pains in the bones." And as he made this solemn pronouncement he winked very, very slowly and solemnly.

The detective returned to the bargaining. "Well—it's a deal, then, I'm satisfied."

But events took a quick turn. The sergeant had done a bit of quick thinking, and before Michael Sullivan replied he chipped in.

" 'Tis the sort of thing that a man wouldn't care to be putting a price on or valuing in money, but I am just thinking that there is nothing in this world would please my missus more than for me to bring her home such a bottle after my visit to Kilbrigid. Her mother always has the sciaticy bad in the winter, and she'll be visiting her next week. I'll go to twenty-five bob for it."

"For a bottle of water from a well?"

"Sure we know that. Haven't I tasted it myself? What else would it be or would I be buying?"

The next station was Michael Sullivan's. He drew the coat round him and started to button it.

"Twenty-seven-and-six," said the detective.

"Twenty-eight-and-six," chipped in the sergeant.

"Twenty-nine shillings," added the detective.

"Twenty-nine-and-six," spoke up the sergeant. "I wouldn't be spoiling a good thought for a miserable shilling or so."

The train drew into the station. Michael Sullivan got up from his seat.

"Here, take the two notes," said the detective, proffering him thirty shillings. Michael Sullivan undid his coat and drew out the bottle. He got the two notes into his fist and handed over the bottle to the detective. "Ye're witnesses, every man of you, that 'tis a bottle of blessed water I'm selling."

"We are, we are," the company chorused. "I suppose that it's his lucky day," added the sergeant with a private wink to Sullivan. "And no man can be beat when the luck runs with him. 'Tis better to be born lucky, I suppose, than to be born intelligent. Good night to you now."

"It's a queer thing, after all," Michael Sullivan thought, as he climbed up the dark mountain track, with the two notes held sweetly in his fingers, "'tis a queer thing, all right, what a power there is in the imagination: that a man should go against the hearing of his own ears and the sense of his own reason because of it. And to think that that is the sort of fellows we have running the country for us, and that's the sort of fellows herself is warning me against. Guards, where are you!"

"Well, I suppose after all your day's traipsing about the countryside you forgot the bottle of water for me," was his wife's greeting as he entered the kitchen.

"I tell you, woman, that I was on business bent and I had no time to be worrying myself about bottles of water. There's a fine spring well outside your own door, if you would only use that and the powers of imagination rightly instead of putting the bad word on everything. Have you the tea ready?"

"The tea is by the fire for you. Wisha! I don't suppose that you'll get sense till the guards catch you and charge you dearly for the teaching of you."

"Guards, me eye!" Michael Sullivan laughed. "To hear the talk by you one would think that I was only born yesterday. Guards teach me, indeed! 'Tis the clever guard will be the match for Michael Sullivan—or detective either."

Giovanni Guareschi

TWO BAPTISMS

HUNGER STRIKE

Smilzo's mother had paralyzed legs, but she also had a head
on her shoulders, and even though she had been confined to
a chair for five or six years, she knew exactly what was going
on. When she was present, Smilzo and his wife didn't dare talk
politics, but she had a keen ear and heard much of what they
didn't even say. They thought they had everything under control, but a few days after their son was born the old woman
came out and said:

"It's time to baptize him."

Smilzo was taken by surprise and stood there gaping, but his
wife jumped into the breach.

"There's no hurry," she said. "Let's wait at least until this
cold spell is over."

The old woman said nothing, but two days later she at-
tacked again.

"Well, is he going to be baptized or isn't he?"

With the passage of time she became more and more in-
sistent, and finally Smilzo screwed up his courage to say:
"Don't let's hear any more talk about this business of baptism.
Times have changed in a great many ways that you don't
know."

The old woman shook her head. "From the day when Jesus
Christ started this business of baptism, times have changed
over and over and any number of things have happened, but
newborn babies have always been baptized."

Smilzo muttered something about political parties and excommunications, but the old woman knew what she was talking about and stuck to it.

"Newborn babies aren't party members. And so they've got to be baptized."

Smilzo repeated that she didn't understand, but she went on shaking her head.

"I understand perfectly well. Your father was worse than you are when it comes to political notions, but you were baptized shortly after you were born."

"Things were different in those days," Smilzo's wife exclaimed.

"And wives were different too!" retorted the old woman.

"Wives were different? What do you mean? What have you got against me?"

"The fact that you're a silly girl."

"All right, then," the wife shouted. "I won't have my baby baptized, for certain. If when he's older, he feels like being baptized, then he can do something about it."

The old woman looked at her son, but he failed to agree with her.

"It's putting something over on children to baptize them when they don't know what it's all about," he mumbled.

"Very well," said the old woman. "From now on, I'm not eating. I shan't eat until the baby's been baptized."

"You'll starve for years, then," said her daughter-in-law with a mocking laugh.

Smilzo said nothing, but brought his fist down on the table and went out of the house.

The next day the old woman did not drink her usual cup of milk for breakfast and at noon she sat quietly in her chair, watching the others eat their lunch. It was the same thing at supper, and finally Smilzo lost his patience.

"You've behaved quite long enough like a spoiled child," he said. "Go ahead and eat, instead of trying to upset me."

"She'll eat when she's hungry," his wife reassured him. But

another day went by in the same way, and the daughter-in-law began to be worried.

"We must call the doctor," she said, "tell him what's happened, and have her taken away. Otherwise, if she dies of starvation, we'll be blamed for it. Can't you see her little game? She wants to ruin our reputation."

At this point the old woman spoke up.

"Give me pen and paper and I'll write down that I'm dying of my own free will. I'm not trying to ruin your reputation; I simply want to save my grandson's soul."

Smilzo's wife had an attack of nerves and began sobbing: "She hates me! I won't have any milk for the baby if she goes on this way."

"What of it?" said the old woman. "Snake's milk won't do him any good."

Smilzo ran out of the house in despair. But he could just as well have stayed home, because the old woman did not open her mouth to speak again. The third day she chose to stay in bed.

"I'd rather die in this position," she explained. "Please call the priest."

"No!" shouted her daughter-in-law. "No!"

"It doesn't really matter," said the old woman. "God will listen to me just the same."

"You'll die with a curse upon you!" shouted her daughter-in-law. "It's a clear-cut case of suicide, because you won't eat."

"No, you've prevented me from eating by refusing to have the baby baptized."

She closed her eyes and sank back on the pillows, while her daughter-in-law withdrew uneasily. Smilzo had been listening just outside the door.

"Something must be done in a hurry," he said.

"Are you going to give in to the priests?" his wife panted. "They've thrown you out of the Church and you ask them to baptize your son? That doesn't go very well with the beliefs you profess in public."

"Take it easy!" said Smilzo. "We've got to find a way to kill two birds with one stone. I'm going to see Peppone."

Peppone was in his workshop when Smilzo burst in upon him.

"Chief, you've got to help me. I'm in hot water." He proceeded to tell his thorny story and concluded: "Chief, I don't want to betray my political principles, but I can't let my mother die. Suppose I get a fancy, lace-trimmed baptismal dress; you put on your best clothes and come for us in your car. We'll have the baby all rigged out in white and show him to his grandmother, with you in a godfather's role. We'll drive to the People's Palace, sneak in through the courtyard, drink a bottle of wine, and then go back and say to my mother: 'Here he is, fresh from the font, just as you wanted!' Then she'll start eating again and my conscience will be clear."

"I see," said Peppone. "But what if she ever finds out?"

"She won't," said Smilzo curtly. "And the main thing just now is to get her to eat."

Peppone shrugged but agreed to co-operate, and while Smilzo went to buy a robe he put on his best clothes. Half an hour later they were at Smilzo's house. The house was in a lonely spot, and there was a heavy fog in the air, both of them favorable circumstances. Smilzo's wife ran to wake up the old woman.

"If you really don't want to ruin our reputation, then get up for a minute. The baby's godfather is here."

"His godfather?" exclaimed the old woman, opening her eyes wide.

"Yes, the mayor himself, who's honored us by consenting to present him for baptism."

Voices rang out downstairs, and the old woman pulled herself into an upright position and threw a shawl around her shoulders.

"Where's the baby?" she asked.

"They're dressing him now."

"Is he fitted out properly?"

"You'll soon see."

There was a knock at the door, and Smilzo came in, carrying the baby wrapped in the most elaborate outfit that can be imagined. Behind this dazzling white vision was the massive figure of Peppone. But the old woman had eyes only for the baby.

"What a little beauty!" she sobbed, raising her gaunt hands as if before some miraculous apparition.

Even the mother was amazed to see her child in such festive array. She snatched him out of Smilzo's arms in order to smooth out the pleats and straighten the bows of the baptismal robe and put the cap at the proper angle on the tiny pink head.

"How are you?" Peppone asked the old woman.

At last she managed to take her eyes off the baby and look at Peppone.

"What an honor you are paying us, Mr. Mayor!" she exclaimed, grasping one of his big paws. "God bless you! I know it's thanks to you that my son came around to reason. But never mind about that; it's all over . . ."

Peppone tried to free his hand, but she held it in an iron grasp.

"Don't say that!" he replied. "Your son doesn't need advice from anybody. He's a fine man. And the honor of being his child's godfather is all mine . . . But tell me how you are feeling."

"Splendid, thank you," she answered. "I had a touch of flu, just like everyone else this winter, but I'm quite well now."

"Take good care of yourself!" Peppone admonished her in an authoritative tone. And after this he could find nothing else to say.

"We must hurry along," put in Smilzo. "The priest is waiting."

The old woman insisted on looking at the baby again and laid a finger on his forehead.

"He's smiling!" said Peppone. "Seems as if he knew you already."

The baby had clutched the old woman's hand, and for a moment he would not let it go.

"He wants me to come along," she sighed, "but I'm in no condition to go. When I hear the church bells ring I'll be happy."

"You may not hear them at all," mumbled her daughter-in-law nervously. "There's a fog outside so thick you could cut it with a knife."

"I've a keen ear, and besides, I'll open the window," the old woman answered, smiling.

In the bar of the People's Palace there was no one but Bigio, who was engaged in going over some accounts. He was startled to see Peppone and Smilzo come in, bearing the decked-out baby.

"Pull down the blinds," said Peppone, "and bring us a bottle of dry white wine."

Bigio brought the bottle of wine and three glasses.

"Aren't you having a drink too?" asked Smilzo.

"Well, there are three of us, aren't there? And I've brought three glasses."

"What about the fourth?" asked Smilzo, pointing with a laugh at the white bundle on the table.

"I don't get it," Bigio said.

"A proletarian baptism!" exclaimed Smilzo, raising his glass. "To the health of a new comrade!"

Bigio and Peppone drained their glasses. Then, while Peppone told Bigio what it was all about, Smilzo dipped his finger into the wine and held it up to the baby's lips.

"Look how he sucks it!" he said proudly. "It's plain he'll grow up to be a very fine fellow!"

The others made no answer, and Smilzo drank down another glass of wine. For several minutes he was absorbed in his thoughts, but finally he said:

"The church bells! She wanted to hear them ringing!"

Just then the church bells actually rang, and the three men jumped as if in the presence of something supernatural.

"Oh, yes," said Bigio. "Today they were going to baptize the druggist's baby."

Smilzo gave a roar of joy.

"She wanted to hear the church bells, did she? Well, there they are! What luck!"

The bundle on the table began to wriggle, and Peppone touched the baby's warm, rosy forehead with his enormous hand. The baby took hold of his middle finger and would not let it go. Peppone reflected that a short time before the baby had held his grandmother's old hand in the same way. Now the baby held fast again. Meanwhile Smilzo drank a third glass of wine.

"We can go home now," he said, slamming the empty glass down on the table.

Peppone and Bigio did not move.

"Ring down the curtain!" said Smilzo. "The play is over, and I'm a perfect swine."

Peppone and Bigio had never heard what the Party calls confession couched in such very honest and appropriate terms.

"Go to it, Bigio," said Peppone, "and make it snappy."

And Bigio was off like a shot.

"What's this?" asked Don Camillo, going over to the baptismal font.

"My son!" said Smilzo, straightening the ribbons which stuck out of the bundle on Peppone's arm.

"Poor boy!" sighed Don Camillo. "Couldn't he have chosen a better father?"

The baby was in good form by now and proceeded to grasp Don Camillo's middle finger. "Brat!" Don Camillo said severely. "Are you trying to take other people's belongings away from them so soon?"

Smilzo wanted to say something, but Don Camillo drowned out his voice.

"Silence! As you know, no convinced Communist can serve as a godfather. Are you a convinced Communist, Peppone?"

"No sir!" said Peppone.

"God only knows whether you are telling the truth, and He'll call you to account for it on Judgment Day."

After the ceremony was over and Peppone had gone out to the car, in which Bigio was waiting before the church, Smilzo went up to Don Camillo.

"How much do I owe you for your trouble?" he asked.

"Nothing. You, too, can settle your accounts with God Almighty."

Smilzo looked at him with mistrust.

"You won't get my next baby, though!" he said defiantly.

"The future is in God's hands, my son!" said Don Camillo, throwing out his arms. "But get out of here in a hurry, because the present might be in my feet!"

This was a theory just like any other. But Smilzo knew the size and strength of Don Camillo's feet, and so he took it into due consideration.

A BAPTISM

One day Don Camillo, perched high on a ladder, was busily polishing St. Joseph's halo. Unexpectedly a man and two women, one of whom was Peppone's wife, came into the church. Don Camillo turned around to ask what they wanted.

"There is something here to be baptized," replied the man, and one of the women held up a bundle containing a baby.

"Whose is it?" inquired Don Camillo, coming down from his ladder.

"Mine," replied Peppone's wife.

"And your husband's?" persisted Don Camillo.

"Well, naturally! Who else would be the father? You, maybe?" retorted Peppone's wife indignantly.

"No need to be offended," observed Don Camillo on his

way to the sacristy. "I've been told often enough that your party approves of free love."

As he passed before the high altar, Don Camillo knelt down and gave a discreet wink in the direction of Christ. "Did you hear that one?" he murmured with a happy grin. "One in the eye for the Godless ones!"

"Don't talk rubbish, Don Camillo," replied Christ irritably. "If they had no God why should they come here to get their child baptized? If Peppone's wife had boxed your ears it would have served you right."

"If Peppone's wife had boxed my ears I should have taken the three of them by the scruff of their necks and . . ."

"And what?" Christ asked severely.

"Oh, nothing; just a figure of speech," Don Camillo hastened to assure Him, rising to his feet.

"Don Camillo, watch your step," Christ said sternly.

Duly vested, Don Camillo approached the baptismal font. "What do you wish to name this child?" he asked Peppone's wife.

"Lenin Libero Antonio," she replied.

"Then go and get him baptized in Russia," said Don Camillo calmly, replacing the cover on the font.

The priest's hands were as big as shovels, and the three left the church without protest. But as Don Camillo tried to slip into the sacristy he was stopped by the voice of Christ. "Don Camillo, you have done a very wicked thing. Go at once and bring those people back and baptize their child."

"But, Lord," protested Don Camillo, "you really must bear in mind that baptism is a very sacred matter. Baptism is . . ."

"Don Camillo," Christ interrupted him, "are you trying to teach me the nature of baptism? Didn't I invent it? I tell you that you have been guilty of gross presumption, because if that child were to die at this moment it would be your fault if it failed to attain Paradise!"

"Lord, let us not be melodramatic! Why in the name of Heaven should it die? It's as pink and white as a rose!"

"That doesn't mean a thing!" Christ pointed out. "What if

a tile should fall on its head or it suddenly had convulsions? It was your duty to baptize it."

Don Camillo raised his hands in protest. "But, Lord, think it over. If it were certain that the child would go to hell, then we might stretch a point. But since he might easily manage to slip into heaven, in spite of his father, how can You ask me to risk anyone getting in there with a name like Lenin? I'm thinking of the reputation of heaven."

"The reputation of heaven is my business," shouted Christ angrily. "What matters to me is that a man should be a decent fellow, and I care less than nothing whether his name be Lenin or Button. At the very most, you should have pointed out to those people that saddling children with fantastic names may be a nuisance to them when they grow up."

"Very well," replied Don Camillo. "I am always wrong. I'll see what I can do."

Just then someone came into the church. It was Peppone, alone, with the baby in his arms. He closed the church door behind him and bolted it. "I'm not leaving this church," he said, "until my son has been baptized with the name that I have chosen."

"Look at that," whispered Don Camillo, smiling as he turned to Christ. "Now do You see what these people are? One is filled with the holiest intentions, and this is how they treat you."

"Put yourself in his place," Christ replied. "One may not approve of his attitude but one can understand it."

Don Camillo shook his head.

"I have already said that I do not leave this place unless you baptize my son!" repeated Peppone. After laying the bundle containing the baby upon a bench he took off his coat, rolled up his sleeves, and came toward the priest threateningly.

"Lord," implored Don Camillo, "I ask You! If You think one of Your priests should give way to the threats of a layman, then I must obey. But if I do, and tomorrow they bring me a calf and compel me to baptize it, You must not complain. You know very well how dangerous it is to create precedents."

"All right, but in this case you must try to make him understand. . . ."

"And if he hits me?"

"Then you must accept it. You must endure and suffer as I did."

Don Camillo turned to his visitor. "Very well, Peppone," he said. "The baby will leave the church baptized, but not with that accursed name."

"Don Camillo," stuttered Peppone, "don't forget that my stomach has never recovered from that bullet I stopped in the mountains. If you hit low, I go after you with a bench."

"Don't worry, Peppone; I can deal with you entirely in the upper stories," Don Camillo assured him, landing a quick one above his ear.

They were both burly men and their blows whistled through the air. After twenty minutes of speechless and furious combat, Don Camillo distinctly heard a voice behind him.

"No, Don Camillo! A left to the jaw!" It came from Christ above the altar. Don Camillo struck hard and Peppone crashed to the ground.

He remained there for about ten minutes; then he sat up, got to his feet, rubbed his jaw, shook himself, put on his jacket and reknotted his red handkerchief. Then he picked up the baby. Fully vested, Don Camillo was waiting, steady as a rock, beside the font. Peppone approached him slowly.

"What are we going to name him?" asked Don Camillo.

"Camillo Libero Antonio," muttered Peppone.

Don Camillo shook his head. "No; we will name him Libero Camillo Lenin," he said. "After all, the Camillo will cancel out Lenin any day."

"Amen," muttered Peppone, still massaging his jaw.

When all was done and Don Camillo passed before the altar, Christ smiled and remarked: "Don Camillo, I have to admit that in politics you are my master."

"And in boxing," replied Don Camillo with perfect gravity, carelessly fingering a large lump on his forehead.

Joe Coogan

DOUBLE SKULL, SLOW BURN, AND A PING

The Christmas entertainment given annually by the eighth-grade class of St. Theodosia's grammar school in Philadelphia was not an occasion noted for gay and untrammeled revelry. It was usually a sedately religious and pretty dull affair, but the year my brother Willie was in the cast the whole thing acquired a peculiar air of sly debauchery.

Willie referred to it later (much later; he wouldn't let anyone mention it for years) as "that time I dragged a naked woman on stage." This, as you will see, was not a precise description of what happened. But it was close enough.

The year that my brother performed, the direction of the show was under new management. The old eighth-grade teacher had been transferred, and her place was taken by a plump, middle-aged nun named Sister Rose Anita. She was a genial woman with a round, pleasant face, and she carried herself with a certain blithe assurance. An assurance, one felt, that could not be shattered by anything she considered less formidable than the Crack of Doom. The Crack of Doom occurred in the latter part of October.

Sister was in class giving a spirited talk on the adjectival clause when a boy from one of the lower grades knocked on the door, entered, and handed her a small slip of paper. She assigned us some written work to do and left the room. She came back a changed woman. Her face was pale and drawn, and her eyes had a hunted, furtive expression. After she dismissed the class she called me over to her desk. She drummed her fingers on the desk top and spoke in a low, distracted monotone.

"Joseph," she said, "unexpected development. Must get to

the library this afternoon. Important research. I want you to come with me. Help carry some material." She stood up, squared her shoulders, and marched determinedly out of the room. I followed, carrying her brief case.

Inside the library, her courage faltered. She walked slowly over to the drama section and stared irresolutely at the long, crowded shelves. With a pathetic attempt at briskness, she snatched several books at random, read off the titles, and handed them to me. They had names like: *Frolics for Young Folks, Pageants Can Be Fun,* and *The Fourth Wall in Restoration Comedy.* She took out the maximum number allowed and went into the periodical room.

"Young man," she said to the clerk, "do you have any authoritative publication that deals with the production of plays?"

The clerk said that he had. He went back to the files and returned with several thick, heavily bound volumes of newspapers which he placed on a nearby table. Sister sat down, opened one of them, and for the first time that afternoon she smiled.

"*Variety,*" she said, "journal of stage, screen and radio. Why, this may be exactly what I want!" She began to read, and her smile stiffened into an expression of perplexed astonishment.

"You may go, Joseph," she said. "I think I'll be here for some time."

When I left, her head was bent low over the library table and her forefinger moved slowly across the page in front of her.

Sister Rose Anita went to the library every afternoon after that, and gradually her old assurance reappeared. But with a difference. Her voice seemed to have become more assertive, she frequently made obscure references to bygone vaudeville acts, and she began to speak in a strange idiom.

One afternoon, a few weeks before Entertainment time, she stopped me in the hall.

"Joseph," she said, "as a member of the eighth grade you will naturally be expected to take part in the show. This year, however, I'm permitting a slight departure from the rules. I want you and your younger brother William to act together as a unit, a team."

"Are we going to be Wise Men?" I asked.

"Certainly not. You're going to be elves." She leaned forward and her voice became quietly confidential. "At long last," she said, "Saint Theodosia's is going Broadway. You can assure your brother William that our little effort will be very sockeroo." She winked and waddled swiftly down the hall.

My brother was nine years old at the time and in the fifth grade. A thin kid with a mop of unruly brown hair and a long mobile face, he had a high reputation as a mimic (his Durante imitation was particularly well thought of), and it was probably this that led to the singular honor of his being picked for a speaking part in the show. Although a few of the first- and second-grade girls were occasionally used as extras, this was the first time that anyone not in the graduating class had a leading role. Willie was quite set up about it.

"What the hell," he said, "it's better than watching the old thing." He swore a lot when he was excited; a habit he picked up from my father.

A few days after Sister Rose Anita stopped me in the hall, we met in the eighth-grade classroom for our first rehearsal. When we were all seated Sister took a large sheaf of papers from her brief case and paced rapidly back and forth in the front of the room.

"Boys and girls," she said, "we have a lot of work ahead of us if we're going to make this year's Entertainment smash-hit material. I've already taken steps. Instead of the usual show, I've arranged to offer our audience a double feature. This should be a pleasant innovation, as double bills gross high on main stem." She smiled brightly. "We open with a short one-act play which we're going to follow with a fine two-act musical comedy. I'm going to read the play, and I want everyone to pay very close attention. I'm sure it has an important message for each one of us."

The play was an educational skit put out by a local dental

society and entitled, A *Tooth's Best Friend*. It concerned the St. Clair-Uncle Tom-like relationship between one Ancient Molar, member of a proud old tooth family, and Brush, a faithful family retainer. After a rather promising beginning ("Hello, Tooth," "Hello, Brush"), it became sentimentally maudlin and ended with Tooth weeping melodramatically on Brush's shoulder. Sister read it very effectively.

"That will be all for now, children," she said when she had finished. "I haven't time to go over the musical."

As Willie and I were leaving, she beckoned to us.

"I almost forgot," she said. "I have something very important to tell you two." We came back into the room.

"The musical," she said, "is about two elves getting the toys ready for Santa Claus." She pointed to my brother. "You, William, will be elf number one. You're mischievous, spritely, alert. Joseph, you're elf number two—slow, dull witted, but all in all very sincere. You're a foil for William, the minor comedian. What we call the second banana."

Willie and I stared bewilderedly at each other.

"In the second act," she continued, "you have a series of lines which are certain to get a very well-defined yak." She handed us a paper and pointed to the top of the page. "Read from here," she said.

Willie had the first line.

"Well, elf," he began, "did you get the Flit gun ready so we can spray the—"

"Reindeer," Sister prompted.

"Reindeer?"

"Flit?" I said. "Why do you want to spray Flit on the reindeer?"

"Why, so they'll be able to flit over the rooftops, of course!" my brother said.

When Sister Rose Anita finished laughing she turned to me.

"That line's guaranteed to fracture them," she said. "Especially, Joseph, when you top it off with a double skull, slow burn, and a ping."

"Is that something elves do?" I asked.

"It's what almost any comedian who is what we call a B.O. draw can do. I'll show you. William, read the line again."

My brother read the line. Sister walked quickly away from him, scowled, looked back twice (the double skull), ran her right hand slowly over her face (slow burn), jumped up and threw both hands high in the air (the ping).

"Try it," she said.

I did, and it gave me a lot of trouble. I still can't do it very well.

On Entertainment Day the cast met in the auditorium about an hour before curtaintime. With the exception of Nell Lacey, a fat, nervous girl with a deep voice who played Santa Claus, my brother and I were the most impressively outfitted members of the group. My mother had despaired of making elves' suits and had rented them from a local costumer. Willie wore a long green coat, green tights, and a high pointed hat. I had the same outfit in brown. The girls in the chorus of dolls were swathed in some thin gauzelike material, and the boys who represented toy soldiers were dressed simply in white shirts and slacks. A few wore medals.

As Willie and I walked through the auditorium, we were stopped by a lean, somber-looking kid named Harry Snyder. Snyder (Ancient Molar) had on a white cloth hat that vaguely resembled a tooth and he wore a long, fuzzy gray beard. He inspected us critically.

"You look pretty silly," he said, but we could tell he was jealous.

Sister Rose Anita lined us up and placed each one in his correct position either on- or off-stage. This was important, as the stage was a shallow one with no crossover in back. On the left side there was a door leading to the main building and a screen which shielded the curtain puller. Off-stage right was shaped like a large square box with one opening which led directly to the playing area.

As we took our places we could hear the menacing murmur of the helplessly reluctant audience being herded into the narrow auditorium.

After Sister had us arranged properly she made a final check on each costume. When she came to me, she frowned.

"Technically speaking, Joseph," she said, "you're not really an elf at all. You're a brownie." Snyder sneered.

Sister started to say something else, but she was interrupted by the voices of children singing the school song. They sounded surly.

"On your toes, boys and girls," she said. "Monsignor Blake has arrived." Monsignor Blake was the local pastor and the perennial honored guest at these functions.

When the singing died down, Sister gave us a few final instructions. "Remember now, make it big, loud, and wait for the laughs." She walked over to the prompter's chair at stage right.

The opening skit was played in front of the curtain to desultory applause. Brush and Tooth came off-stage. Sister Claire, the music teacher, played a few introductory chords on the piano and the musical began.

Willie and I had the first song.

> We're Santa's helpers. We're true blue,
> Elf number one, and elf number two.
> We work with paint and nails and glue,
> So that the toys will get to you,
> Early Christmas morning.

We did a rapid, shuffling dance, stopped and bowed deeply. There wasn't a sound from the front of the house.

After about ten minutes of light banter punctuated by long and silence-filled pauses for laughs, we wound up the toy soldiers and they paraded around the stage for a while. Then Willie grabbed a large, rouge-filled paint can and scampered over to the dolls.

"Paint 'em on the cheek, and paint 'em quick. Gotta get ready for Old Saint Nick," he said.

His voice sounded loud and ill tempered. I could tell he was ruffled by the lack of audience response.

He dipped a large brush in the can and capered fantastically down the row of dolls, patting each one lightly on the cheek and then skipping wildly to the next. He was putting his heart into it.

The last doll in line, a little wide-eyed first-grade girl, watched this antic progress with considerable misgiving. When he leaned over to tap her on the cheek with the brush, she let out a terrified shriek and raced frantically away from him. Willie, reaching out to stop her, caught the skirt of her light gauze dress. There was a soft tearing sound and the panic-stricken child, clad only in brief panties, stood petrified in the center of the stage. The audience cheered.

One of the older girls picked up the denuded doll and carried her off-stage.

Willie dropped the paint can, walked stiffly and mechanically over to me, and grabbed me by the shoulder. His eyes had a blank, horrified look, and his hand trembled.

"What did you do with the Flit?" he shouted.

This dexterous leap from the opening to the climax of Act Two was more than I could cope with.

"Flit?" I asked weakly.

"To make them flit better, dopey," he said.

I remembered the routine. I glared at him, walked away, and looked back. His next line was spoken in a loud, clear voice.

"You forgot the damn ping," he said.

The audience was hushed in awe-struck wonder. Although I could see and hear what was going on with almost preternatural acuteness, I felt powerless to speak or move and could only stare at him with an expression of slack-jawed idiocy. This seemed to unnerve him.

Sister Rose Anita bounced angrily out of the prompter's box and pointed to the chorus.

"Sing," she said. "For heaven's sake, sing!"

Willie, who by this time was in a state approaching madness, thought she was pleading with him. He ran through a quick and rather skillful chorus of "Inka Dinka Doo" and then began the only other song he knew, an Irish Come-all-ye that he had picked up from my grandfather.

"She was a great big lump of an Irish agricultural girl, and, oh, how I'd like to tie her garter," were the opening words. Sister Claire played "Holy Night" on the piano loudly.

Sister Rose Anita kept shouting, "Curtain! Curtain!" but to no avail. She seized Harry Snyder, shouted something to him, and pushed him in the direction of stage left.

When Snyder got in front of the audience he did his duty as he saw it. He stood at attention and his face assumed a haughty, aristocratic look.

"The thief of time cannot destroy my treasure trove of calcium!" he said. It was his big speech from the one-act play.

Sister Rose Anita rushed over to Nell Lacey and tried to force her on stage. Meanwhile old Ancient Molar was giving it all he had.

Oh, faithful squire of every stalwart tooth,
Brave Brush, you do not deign to stand aloof,
But help avert life's sad decaying end.
You are, in truth, brave Brush—a tooth's best Friend.

Sister Rose Anita did a perfectly executed slow burn and a ping. Then, infected by the general lunacy of the moment, she snatched the Santa Claus mask from Nell Lacey, held it over her face with one hand, and raced across the stage.

"Merry Christmas, elves! Merry Christmas, toys! Merry Christmas, children!" she said. When she reached stage left, she pulled the curtain and leaned heavily against the wall. The mask had dropped to the floor; she shook her head slowly from side to side, and her eyes were filled with tears.

"What a turkey. What a flopperoo," she said dispiritedly.

A few members of the cast muttered some semiarticulate words of commiseration, but most of us stood glumly silent, envisioning God knows what dark reprisals that were bound to follow the afternoon's performance.

The only sounds from the auditorium were the slow, threatening footsteps of Monsignor Blake as he approached the stage to give his annual Christmas speech. He was an old man with a tired, dour face (I had only seen him at Entertainment time) and he had a reputation as a stern disciplinarian. Our only hope was that he wouldn't expel us publicly.

"My dear children," he began, and his voice had a strange, choked quality. "I'm sure we're all greatly edified by the amount of time and energy put into today's performance. I suggest we show our appreciation by applause."

The house went wild. There were cheers, whistles, shouts, and long-sustained clapping.

"What the hell," my brother said, "we're a hit!"

Sister Rose Anita glared at him but as the applause mounted her eyes became soft and dreamy and she threw her head back proudly.

"You see, boys and girls, you never can tell," she said. "That's show biz. It most certainly is show biz."

We took five curtain calls.

Stephen Vincent Benét

O'HALLORAN'S LUCK

They were strong men built the Big Road, in the early days of America, and it was the Irish did it. My grandfather, Tim O'Halloran, was a young man then, and wild. He could swing a pick all day and dance all night, if there was a fiddler handy; and if there was a girl to be pleased, he pleased her, for he had the tongue and the eye. Likewise, if there was a man to be stretched, he could stretch him with the one blow.

I saw him later on in years when he was thin and white-headed, but in his youth he was not so. A thin, whiteheaded man would have had little chance, and they driving the Road to the West. It was two-fisted men cleared the plains and bored through the mountains. They came in the thousands to do it from every county in Ireland; and now the names are not known. But it's over their graves you pass, when you ride in the Pullmans. And Tim O'Halloran was one of them, six feet high and solid as the Rock of Cashel when he stripped to the skin.

He needed to be all of that, for it was not easy labor. 'Twas a time of great booms and expansions in the railroad line, and they drove the tracks north and south, east and west, as if the devil was driving behind. For this they must have the boys with shovel and pick, and every immigrant ship from Ireland was crowded with bold young men. They left famine and England's rule behind them—and it was the thought of many they'd pick up gold for the asking in the free States of America, though it's little gold that most of them ever saw. They found themselves up to their necks in the water of the canals, and burned black by the suns of the prairie—and that was a great surprise to them. They saw their sisters and their mothers made servants that had not been servants in Ireland, and that was a strange change too. Eh, the death and the broken hopes it takes to make a country! But those with the heart and the tongue kept the tongue and the heart.

Tim O'Halloran came from Clonmelly, and he was the fool of the family and the one who listened to tales. His brother Ignatius went for a priest, and his brother James for a sailor, but they knew he could not do those things. He was strong and biddable and he had the O'Halloran tongue; but there came a time of famine, when the younger mouths cried for bread and there was little room in the nest. He was not entirely wishful to emigrate, and yet, when he thought of it, he was wishful. 'Tis often enough that way with a younger son. Perhaps he was the more wishful because of Kitty Malone.

'Tis a quiet place, Clonmelly, and she'd been the light of it to him. But now the Malones had gone to the States of America—and it was well known that Kitty had a position there the like of which was not to be found in all Dublin Castle. They called her a hired girl, to be sure, but did not she eat from gold plates, like all the citizens of America? And when she stirred her tea, was not the spoon made of gold? Tim O'Halloran thought of this and of the chances and adventures that a bold young man might find, and at last he went to the boat. There were many from Clonmelly on that boat, but he kept himself to himself and dreamed his own dreams.

The more disillusion it was to him, when the boat landed him in Boston and he found Kitty Malone there, scrubbing the stairs of an American house with a pail and brush by her side. But that did not matter, after the first, for her cheeks still had the rose in them and she looked at him in the same way. 'Tis true there was an Orangeman courting her—conductor he was on the horsecars, and Tim did not like that. But after Tim had seen her, he felt himself the equal of giants; and when the call came for strong men to work in the wilds of the West, he was one of the first to offer. They broke a sixpence between them before he left—it was an English sixpence, but that did not matter greatly to them. And Tim O'Halloran was going to make his fortune, and Kitty Malone to wait for him, though her family liked the Orangeman best.

Still and all, it was cruel work in the West, as such work must be, and Tim O'Halloran was young. He liked the strength and the wildness of it—he'd drink with the thirstiest and fight with the wildest—and that he knew how to do. It was all meat and drink to him—the bare tracks pushing ahead across the bare prairie and the fussy cough of the wood-burning locomotives and the cold blind eyes of a murdered man looking up at the prairie stars. And then there was the cholera and the malaria—and the strong man you'd worked on the grade beside, all of a sudden gripping his belly with the fear of death on his face and his shovel falling to the ground.

Next day he would not be there and they'd scratch a name from the payroll. Tim O'Halloran saw it all.

He saw it all and it changed his boyhood and hardened it. But, for all that, there were times when the black fit came upon him, as it does to the Irish, and he knew he was alone in a strange land. Well, that's a hard hour to get through, and he was young. There were times when he'd have given all the gold of the Americas for a smell of Clonmelly air or a glimpse of Clonmelly sky. Then he'd drink or dance or fight or put a black word on the foreman, just to take the aching out of his mind. It did not help him with his work and it wasted his pay; but it was stronger than he, and not even the thought of Kitty Malone could stop it. 'Tis like that, sometimes.

Well, it happened one night he was coming back from the place where they sold the potheen, and perhaps he'd had a trifle more of it than was advisable. Yet he had not drunk it for that, but to keep the queer thoughts from his mind. And yet, the more that he drank, the queerer were the thoughts in his head. For he kept thinking of the Luck of the O'Hallorans and the tales his granda had told about it in the old country—the tales about pookas and banshees and leprechauns with long white beards.

"And that's a queer thing to be thinking, and myself at labor with a shovel on the open prairies of America," he said to himself. "Sure, creatures like that might live and thrive in the old country—and I'd be the last to deny it—but 'tis obvious they could not live here. The first sight of Western America would scare them into conniptions. And as for the Luck of the O'Hallorans, 'tis little good I've had of it, and me not even able to rise to foreman and marry Kitty Malone. They called me the fool of the family in Clonmelly, and I misdoubt but they were right. Tim O'Halloran, you're a worthless man, for all your strong back and arms." It was with such black, bitter thoughts as these that he went striding over the prairie. And it was just then that he heard the cry in the grass.

'Twas a strange little piping cry, and only the half of it human. But Tim O'Halloran ran to it, for in truth he was spoiling for a fight. Now this will be a beautiful young lady, he said to himself as he ran, and I will save her from robbers; and her father, the rich man, will ask me—but, wirra, 'tis not her I wish to marry, 'tis Kitty Malone. Well, he'll set me up in business, out of friendship and gratitude, and then I will send for Kitty. . . .

But by then he was out of breath, and by the time he had reached the place where the cry came from he could see that it was not so. It was only a pair of young wolf cubs, and they chasing something small and helpless and playing with it as a cat plays with a mouse. Where the wolf cub is, the old wolves are not far, but Tim O'Halloran felt as bold as a lion. "Be off with you!" he cried and he threw a stick and a stone. They ran away into the night, and he could hear them howling—a lonesome sound. But he knew the camp was near, so he paid small attention to that, but looked for the thing they'd been chasing.

It scuttled in the grass but he could not see it. Then he stooped down and picked something up, and when he had it in his hand he stared at it unbelieving. For it was a tiny shoe, no bigger than a child's. And more than that, it was not the kind of shoe that is made in America. Tim O'Halloran stared and stared at it—and at the silver buckle upon it—and still he could not believe.

"If I'd found this in the old country," he said to himself, half aloud, "I'd have sworn that it was a leprechaun's and looked for the pot of gold. But here, there's no chance of that—"

"I'll trouble you for the shoe," said a small voice close by his feet.

Tim O'Halloran stared round him wildly. "By the piper that played before Moses!" he said. "Am I drunk beyond comprehension? Or am I mad? For I thought that I heard a voice."

"So you did, silly man," said the voice again, but irritated, "and I'll trouble you for my shoe, for it's cold in the dewy grass."

"Honey," said Tim O'Halloran, beginning to believe his ears, "honey dear, if you'll but show yourself—"

"I'll do that and gladly," said the voice; and with that the grasses parted, and a little old man with a long white beard stepped out. He was perhaps the size of a well-grown child, as O'Halloran could see clearly by the moonlight on the prairie; moreover, he was dressed in the clothes of antiquity, and he carried cobblers' tools in the belt at his side.

"By faith and belief, but it *is* a leprechaun!" cried O'Halloran, and with that he made a grab for the apparition. For you must know, in case you've been ill brought up, that a leprechaun is a sort of cobbler fairy, and each one knows the whereabouts of a pot of gold. Or it's so they say in the old country. For they say you can tell a leprechaun by his long white beard and his cobbler's tools; and once you have the possession of him, he must tell you where his gold is hid.

The little old man skipped out of his reach as nimbly as a cricket. "Is this Clonmelly courtesy?" he said with a shake in his voice, and Tim O'Halloran felt ashamed.

"Sure, I didn't mean to hurt your worship at all," he said, "but if you're what you seem to be, well then, there's the little matter of a pot of gold—"

"Pot of gold!" said the leprechaun, and his voice was hollow and full of scorn. "And would I be here today if I had that same? Sure, it all went to pay my sea passage, as you might expect."

"Well," said Tim O'Halloran, scratching his head, for that sounded reasonable enough, "that may be so, or again it may not be so. But—"

"Oh, 'tis bitter hard," said the leprechaun, and his voice was weeping, "to come to the waste, wild prairies all alone, just for the love of Clonmelly folk—and then to be disbelieved by the first that speaks to me! If it had been an Ulsterman now, I might have expected it. But the O'Hallorans wear the green."

"So they do," said Tim O'Halloran, "and it shall not be said of an O'Halloran that he denied succor to the friendless. I'll not touch you."

"Do you swear it?" said the leprechaun.

"I swear it," said Tim O'Halloran.

"Then I'll just creep under your coat," said the leprechaun, "for I'm near destroyed by the chills and damps of the prairie. Oh, this weary emigrating!" he went on, with a sigh like a furnace. "'Tis not what it's cracked up to be."

Tim O'Halloran took off his own coat and wrapped it around him. Then he could see him closer—and it could not be denied that the leprechaun was a pathetic sight. He'd a queer little boyish face under the long white beard, but his clothes were all torn and ragged and his cheeks looked hollow with hunger.

"Cheer up!" said Tim O'Halloran and patted him on the back. "It's a bad day that beats the Irish. But tell me first how you came here—that still sticks in my throat."

"And would I be staying behind with half Clonmelly on the water?" said the leprechaun stoutly. "By the bones of Finn, what sort of a man do you think I am?"

"That's well said," said Tim O'Halloran. "And yet I never heard of the Good People emigrating before."

"True for you," said the leprechaun. "The climate here's

not good for most of us and that's a fact. There's a boggart or so that came over with the English, but then the Puritan ministers got after them and they had to take to the woods. And I had a word or two, on my way West, with a banshee that lives by Lake Superior—a decent woman she was, but you could see she'd come down in the world. For even the bits of children wouldn't believe in her; when she let out a screech, sure they thought it was a steamboat. I misdoubt she's died since then—she was not in good health when I left her.

"And as for the native spirits—well, you can say what you like, but they're not very comfortable people. I was captive to some of them a week, and they treated me well enough, but they whooped and danced too much for a quiet man, and I did not like the long, sharp knives on them. Oh, I've had the adventures on my way here," he said, "but they're over now, praises be, for I've found a protector at last." And he snuggled closer under O'Halloran's coat.

"Well," said O'Halloran, somewhat taken aback, "I did not think this would be the way of it when I found O'Halloran's Luck that I'd dreamed of so long. For, first I save your life from the wolves; and now, it seems, I must be protecting you further. But in the tales it's always the other way round."

"And is the company and conversation of an ancient and experienced creature like myself nothing to you?" said the leprechaun fiercely. "Me that had my own castle at Clonmelly and saw O'Sheen in his pride? Then St. Patrick came—wirra, wirra!—and there was an end to it all. For some of us—the Old Fold of Ireland—he baptized, and some of us he chained with the demons of hell. But I was Lazy Brian, betwixt and between, and all I wanted was peace and a quiet life. So he changed me to what you see—me that had six tall harpers to harp me awake in the morning—and laid a doom upon me for being betwixt and between. I'm to serve Clonmelly folk and follow them wherever they go till I serve the servants of servants in a land at the world's end. And then, perhaps, I'll be given a Christian soul and can follow my own inclinations."

"Serve the servants of servants?" said O'Halloran. "Well, that's a hard riddle to read."

"It is that," said the leprechaun, "for I never once met the servant of a servant in Clonmelly, all the time I've been looking. I doubt but that was in St. Patrick's mind."

"If it's criticizing the good saint you are, I'll leave you here on the prairie," said Tim O'Halloran.

"I'm not criticizing him," said the leprechaun with a sigh, "but I could wish he'd been less hasty. Or more specific too; 'tis a great responsibility, and one I never thought to shoulder. But since you've asked for help, you must have it. Only there's just this to be said. There's little money in my pocket."

"Sure, 'tis not for your money I've come to you," said the leprechaun joyously. "And I'll stick closer than a brother."

"I've no doubt of that," said O'Halloran with a wry laugh. "Well, clothes and food I can get for you—but if you stick with me, you must work as well. And perhaps the best way would be for you to be my young nephew Rory, run away from home to work on the railroad."

"And how would I be your young nephew Rory, and me with a long white beard?"

"Well," said Tim O'Halloran with a grin, "as it happens, I've got a razor in my pocket."

And with that you should have heard the leprechaun. He stamped and he swore and he pled—but it was no use at all. If he was to follow Tim O'Halloran, he must do it on Tim O'Halloran's terms, and no two ways about it. So O'Halloran shaved him at last, by the light of the moon, to the leprechaun's great horror, and when he got him back to the construction camp and fitted him out in some old duds of his own —well, it wasn't exactly a boy he looked, but it was more like a boy than anything else. Tim took him up to the foreman the next day and got him signed on for a water boy, and it was a beautiful tale he told the foreman. As well, too, that he had the O'Halloran tongue to tell it with, for when the foreman first looked at young Rory you could see him gulp like a man that's seen a ghost.

"And now what do we do?" said the leprechaun to Tim when the interview was over.

"Why, you work," said Tim with a great laugh, "and Sundays you wash your shirt."

"Thank you for nothing," said the leprechaun with an angry gleam in his eye. "It was not for that I came here from Clonmelly."

"Oh, we've all come here for great fortune," said Tim, "but it's hard to find that same. Would you rather be with the wolves?"

"Oh, no," said the leprechaun.

"Then drill, ye tarrier, drill!" said Tim O'Halloran and shouldered his shovel, while the leprechaun trailed behind.

At the end of the day the leprechaun came to him.

"I've never done mortal work before," he said, "and there's no bone in my body that's not a pain and an anguish to me."

"You'll feel better after supper," said O'Halloran. "And the night's made for sleep."

"But where will I sleep?" said the leprechaun.

"In the half of my blanket," said Tim, "for are you not young Rory, my nephew?"

It was not what he could have wished, but he saw he could do no otherwise. Once you start a tale, you must play up to the tale.

But that was only the beginning, as Tim O'Halloran soon found out. For Tim O'Halloran had tasted many things before, but nor responsibility, and now responsibility was like a bit in his mouth. It was not so bad the first week, while the leprechaun was still ailing. But when, what with the food and the exercise, he began to recover his strength, 'twas a wonder Tim O'Halloran's hair did not turn gray overnight. He was not a bad creature, the leprechaun, but he had all the natural mischief of a boy of twelve and, added to that, the craft and knowledge of generations.

There was the three pipes and the pound of shag the leprechaun stole from McGinnis—and the dead frog he slipped in the foreman's tea—and the bottle of potheen he got hold

of one night, when Tim had to hold his head in a bucket of
water to sober him up. A fortunate thing it was that St. Patrick had left him no great powers, but at that he had enough
to put the jumping rheumatism on Shaun Kelly for two days—
and it wasn't till Tim threatened to deny him the use of his
razor entirely that he took off the spell.

That brought Rory to terms, for by now he'd come to take
a queer pleasure in playing the part of a boy and he did not
wish to have it altered.

Well, things went on like this for some time, and Tim
O'Halloran's savings grew; for whenever the drink was running he took no part in it, for fear of mislaying his wits when
it came to deal with young Rory. And as it was with the
drink, so was it with other things—till Tim O'Halloran began
to be known as a steady man. And then, as it happened one
morning, Tim O'Halloran woke up early. The leprechaun had
finished his shaving and was sitting cross-legged, chuckling
to himself.

"And what's your source of amusement so early in the day?"
said Tim sleepily.

"Oh," said the leprechaun, "I'm just thinking of the rare
hard work we'll have when the line's ten miles farther on."

"And why should it be harder there than it is here?" said
Tim.

"Oh, nothing," said the leprechaun, "but those fools of
surveyors have laid out the line where there's hidden springs
of water. And when we start digging, there'll be the devil to
pay."

"Do you know that for a fact?" said Tim.

"And why wouldn't I know it?" said the leprechaun. "Me
that can hear the water run underground."

"Then what should we do?" said Tim.

"Shift the line half a mile to the west and you'd have a firm
roadbed," said the leprechaun.

Tim O'Halloran said no more at the time. But for all that,
he managed to get to the assistant engineer in charge of construction at the noon hour. He could not have done it before,

but now he was known as a steady man. Nor did he tell where he got the information—he put it on having seen a similar thing in Clonmelly.

Well, the engineer listened to him and had a test made—and sure enough, they struck the hidden spring. "That's clever work, O'Halloran," said the engineer. "You've saved us time and money. And now how would you like to be foreman of a gang?"

"I'd like it well," said Tim O'Halloran.

"Then you boss Gang Five from this day forward," said the engineer. "And I'll keep my eye on you. I like a man that uses his head."

"Can my nephew come with me," said Tim, "for, 'troth, he's my responsibility?"

"He can," said the engineer, who had children of his own.

So Tim got promoted, and the leprechaun along with him. And the first day on the new work, young Rory stole the gold watch from the engineer's pocket, because he liked the tick of it, and Tim had to threaten him with fire and sword before he'd put it back.

Well, things went on like this for another while, till finally Tim woke up early on another morning and heard the leprechaun laughing.

"And what are you laughing at?" he said.

"Oh, the more I see of mortal work, the less reason there is to it," said the leprechaun. "For I've been watching the way they get the rails up to us on the line. And they do it thus and so. But if they did it so and thus, they could do it in half the time with half the work."

"Is that so indeed?" said Tim O'Halloran, and he made him explain it clearly. Then, after he'd swallowed his breakfast, he was off to his friend the engineer.

"That's a clever idea, O'Halloran," said the engineer. "We'll try it." And a week after that, Tim O'Halloran found himself with a hundred men under him and more responsibility than he'd ever had in his life. But it seemed little to him beside the responsibility of the leprechaun, and now the engineer began to lend him books to study and he studied them at nights while the leprechaun snored in its blanket.

A man could rise rapidly in those days—and it was then Tim O'Halloran got the start that was to carry him far. But he did not know he was getting it, for his heart was near broken at the time over Kitty Malone. She'd written him a letter or two when he first came West, but now there were no more of them and at last he got a word from her family telling him he should not be disturbing Kitty with letters from a laboring man. That was bitter for Tim O'Halloran, and he'd think about Kitty and the Orangeman in the watches of the night and groan. And then, one morning, he woke up after such a night and heard the leprechaun laughing.

"And what are you laughing at now?" he said sourly. "For my heart's near burst with its pain."

"I'm laughing at a man that would let a cold letter keep him from his love, and him with pay in his pocket and the contract ending the first," said the leprechaun.

Tim O'Halloran struck one hand in the palm of the other.

"By the piper, but you've the right of it, you queer little creature!" he said. "'Tis back to Boston we go when this job's over."

It was laborer Tim O'Halloran that had come to the West, but it was Railroadman Tim O'Halloran that rode back East in the cars like a gentleman, with a free pass in his pocket and the promise of a job on the railroad that was fitting a married man. The leprechaun, I may say, gave some trouble in the cars, more particularly when he bit a fat woman that called him a dear little boy; but what with giving him peanuts all the way, Tim O'Halloran managed to keep him fairly quieted.

When they got to Boston he fitted them both out in new clothes from top to toe. Then he gave the leprechaun some money and told him to amuse himself for an hour or so while he went to see Kitty Malone.

He walked into the Malones' flat as bold as brass, and there sure enough, in the front room were Kitty Malone and the Orangeman. He was trying to squeeze her hand, and she refusing, and it made Tim O'Halloran's blood boil to see that. But when Kitty saw Tim O'Halloran she let out a scream.

"Oh, Tim!" she said. "Tim! And they told me you were dead in the plains of the West!"

"And a great pity that he was not," said the Orangeman, blowing out his chest with the brass buttons on it, "but a bad penny always turns up."

"Bad penny is it, you brass-buttoned son of iniquity," said Tim O'Halloran. "I have but the one question to put you. Will you stand or will you run?"

"I'll stand as we stood at Boyne Water," said the Orangeman, grinning ugly. "And whose backs did we see that day?"

"Oh, is that the tune?" said Tim O'Halloran. "Well, I'll give you a tune to match it. Who fears to speak of Ninety-Eight?"

With that he was through the Orangeman's guard and stretched him at the one blow, to the great consternation of the Malones. The old woman started to screech and Pat Malone to talk of policemen, but Tim O'Halloran silenced the both of them.

"Would you be giving your daughter to an Orangeman that works on the horsecars, when she might be marrying a future railroad president?" he said. And with that he pulled his savings out of his pocket and the letter that promised the job for a married man. That quieted the Malones a little and, once they got a good look at Tim O'Halloran, they began to change their tune. So, after they'd got the Orangeman out of the house—and he did not go willing, but he went as a whipped man must—Tim O'Halloran recounted all of his adventures.

The tale did not lose in the telling, though he did not speak of the leprechaun, for he thought that had better be left to a later day; and at the end Pat Malone was offering him a cigar. "But I find I have none upon me," said he with a wink at Tim, "so I'll just run down to the corner."

"And I'll go with you," said Kitty's mother, "for if Mr. O'Halloran stays to supper—and he's welcome—there's a bit of shopping to be done."

So the old folks left Tim O'Halloran and his Kitty alone. But just as they were in the middle of their planning and contriving for the future, there came a knock on the door.

"What's that?" said Kitty, but Tim O'Halloran knew well enough and his heart sank within him. He opened the door—and sure enough, it was the leprechaun.

"Well, Uncle Tim," said the creature, grinning, "I'm here."

Tim O'Halloran took a look at him as if he saw him for the first time. He was dressed in new clothes, to be sure, but there was soot on his face and his collar had thumbmarks on it already. But that wasn't what made the difference. New clothes or old, if you looked at him for the first, you could see he was an unchancy thing and not like Christian souls.

"Kitty," he said, "Kitty darling, I had not told you. But this is my young nephew Rory that lives with me."

Well, Kitty welcomed the boy with her prettiest manners, though Tim O'Halloran could see her giving him a side look now and then. All the same, she gave him a slice of cake and he tore it apart with his fingers; but in the middle of it he pointed to Kitty Malone.

"Have you made up your mind to marry my Uncle Tim?" he said. "Faith, you'd better, for he's a grand catch."

"Hold your tongue, young Rory," said Tim O'Halloran angrily, and Kitty blushed red. But then she took the next words out of his mouth.

"Let the gossoon be, Tim O'Halloran," she said bravely. "Why shouldn't he speak his mind? Yes, Roryeen—it's I that will be your aunt in the days to come—and a proud woman too."

"Well, that's good," said the leprechaun, cramming the last of the cake in his mouth, "for I'm thinking you'll make a good home for us, once you're used to my ways."

"Is that to be the way of it, Tim?" said Kitty Malone very quietly, but Tim O'Halloran looked at her and knew what was in her mind. And he had the greatest impulse in the world to deny the leprechaun and send him about his business. And yet, when he thought of it, he knew that he could not do it, not even if it meant the losing of Kitty Malone.

"I'm afraid that must be the way of it, Kitty," he said with a groan.

"Then I honor you for it," said Kitty, with her eyes like stars. She went up to the leprechaun and took his hard little hand. "Will you live with us, young Rory?" she said. "For we'd be glad to have you."

"Thank you kindly, Kitty Malone—O'Halloran to be," said the leprechaun. "And you're lucky, Tim O'Halloran—lucky yourself and lucky in your wife. For if you had denied me then, your luck would have left you—and if she had denied me then, 'twould be but half luck for you both. But now the luck will stick to you the rest of your lives. And I'm wanting another piece of cake," said he.

"Well, it's a queer lad you are," said Kitty Malone, but she went for the cake. The leprechaun swung his legs and looked at Tim O'Halloran. "I wonder what keeps my hands off you," said the latter with a groan.

"Fie!" said the leprechaun, grinning, "and would you be lifting the hand to your one nephew? But tell me one thing, Tim O'Halloran, was this wife you're to take ever in domestic service?"

"And what if she was?" said Tim O'Halloran, firing up. "Who thinks the worse of her for that?"

"Not I," said the leprechaun, "for I've learned about mortal labor since I came to this country—and it's an honest thing. But tell me one thing more. Do you mean to serve this wife of yours and honor her through the days of your wedded life?"

"Such is my intention," said Tim, "though what business it is of—"

"Never mind," said the leprechaun.

"Your shoelace is undone, bold man. Command me to tie it up."

"Tie up my shoe, you black-hearted, villainous little anatomy!" thundered Tim O'Halloran, and the leprechaun did so. Then he jumped to his feet and skipped about the room.

"Free! Free!" he piped. "Free at last! For I've served the servants of servants and the doom has no power on me longer. Free, Tim O'Halloran! O'Halloran's Luck is free!"

Tim O'Halloran stared at him, dumb; and even as he stared, the creature seemed to change. He was small, to be sure, and boyish—but you could see the unchancy look leave him and the Christian soul come into his eyes. That was a queer thing to be seen, and a great one too.

"Well," said Tim O'Halloran in a sober voice, "I'm glad for you, Rory. For now you'll be going back to Clonmelly, no doubt—and faith, you've earned the right."

The leprechaun shook his head.

"Clonmelly's a fine, quiet place," said he, "but this country's bolder. I misdoubt it's something in the air—you will not have noticed it, but I've grown two inches and a half since first I met you, and I feel myself growing still. No, it's off to the mines of the West I am, to follow my natural vocation— for they say there are mines out there you could mislay all Dublin Castle in—and wouldn't I like to try! But speaking of that, Tim O'Halloran," he said, "I was not quite honest with you about the pot of gold. You'll find your share behind the door when I've gone. And now good day and long life to you!"

"But, man dear," said Tim O'Halloran, " 'tis not good-by!" For it was then he realized the affection that was in him for the queer little creature.

"No, 'tis not good-by," said the leprechaun. "When you christen your first son, I'll be at his cradle, though you may not see me—and so with your sons' sons and their sons, for O'Halloran's luck's just begun. But we'll part for the present now. For now I'm a Christian soul; I've work to do in the world."

"Wait a minute," said Tim O'Halloran. "For you would not know, no doubt, and you such a new soul. And no doubt you'll be seeing the priest—but a layman can do it in an emergency and I think this is one. I dare not have you leave me— and you not even baptized."

And with that he made the sign of the cross and baptized the leprechaun. He named him Rory Patrick.

" 'Tis not done with all the formalities," he said at the end, "but I'll defend the intention."

"I'm grateful to you," said the leprechaun. "And if there was a debt to be paid, you've paid it back and more."

And with that he was gone somehow, and Tim O'Halloran was alone in the room. He rubbed his eyes. But there was a little sack behind the door, where the leprechaun had left it—and Kitty was coming in with a slice of cake on a plate.

"Well, Tim," she said, "and where's that young nephew of yours?"

So he took her into his arms and told her the whole story. And how much of it she believed, I do not know. But there's one remarkable circumstance. Ever since then, there's always been one Rory O'Halloran in the family, and that one luckier than the lave. And when Tim O'Halloran got to be a railroad president, why, didn't he call his private car "The Leprechaun"? For that matter, they said, when he took his business trips there'd be a small, boyish-looking fellow would be with him now and again. He'd turn up from nowhere, at some odd stop or other, and he'd be let in at once, while the great of the railroad world were kept waiting in the vestibule. And after a while there'd be singing from inside the car.

Brendan Gill

MOTHER COAKLEY'S REFORM

Even in old age, Mother Coakley was as round and smooth-skinned as a ripe chestnut. In her billowing black habit, she had always the air of being about to be caught up in a gust of mountain wind and carried aloft to the sunny, well-scrubbed corner awaiting her in heaven. Despite the mother superior's hints of disapproval, hints which by anyone else would have been taken as commands, Mother Coakley enjoyed playing tennis with the younger convent girls. The tennis court was on the crest of a hill behind the ramshackle wooden buildings which made up the convent chapel and school; and what seemed in the North Carolina town below an agreeable summer breeze approached—on that dusty oblong of root-ribbed and rocky court—the force and temperature of a winter's gale. Luckily, Mother Coakley paid no attention to temperatures, hot or cold. Gathering the full skirts of her habit into her left hand, she scampered about the court like an energetic chipmunk, letting her veil float out behind her in ghostly disarray, and only just showing the tops of her high black shoes. She had learned to play tennis as a novice at the mother house in France, no one knew how many years ago, and she played it unexpectedly well. Like most people who learned the game in the nineteenth century, she felt no real interest in volleying. She was willing to lose point after point in order to attempt a smashing forehand drive, or to drop an occasional cut shot over the net; and when she had succeeded in doing so, the ball being unreturnable, Mother Coakley would drop her racquet and clap her hands in unaffected delight.

She had no use, in fact, for any of the effete mannerisms of latter-day tennis. If she failed to return an opponent's serve,

she never called, "Good shot," but, screwing up her face into
an expression of self-contempt, would announce sharply, "I
should have had it! I should have had it!" As she played, her
cheeks grew more and more deeply suffused with blood.
Though she looked as if she might be about to suffer a stroke,
she never heeded suggestions that it would be sensible to rest
for a few minutes between sets. "I always get to look like
this," she would say, panting heartily. The French neatness
of speech taught her at the mother house in Dijon would then
slur away to a soft Irish brogue. "Sure, I got to look like this
when I was six." Also, as she continued to play, her rosary,
carelessly stuffed inside her heavy black belt, would work
itself loose and flail about her waist until finally, with tears
of excitement streaming down her cheeks and wisps of clipped
gray hair showing at the sides of her wimple, she would be
forced to stop playing. "If I didn't stop now, I'd strangle myself on my own beads," she would say. "But for them, I'd
be playing till dark."

She usually contrived, however, to retire from the game
while she was still winning. This mild vanity was one of the
two or three enormous sins with which she wrestled all but
visibly from year to year. It was noted by the other nuns in
the convent that Mother Coakley spent more than twice as
much time in the confessional during the height of the tennis
season as she did during the rest of the year. They never commented on this directly, but sometimes they would tease her,
out of love and curiosity, as she left the chapel. "Goodness, you
took a long time saying your penance," they would whisper,
climbing the steep, worn stairs to their cells. "Father Nailer
must have been in a dreadful temper by the time you reached
him." Mother Coakley, who, after Mother Bonnet, was the
oldest nun in age and point of service in the convent, would
flush and answer, in a pretext of anger, "*Attendez!* What kind
of talk is that? *Vous savez les règles!*"

Mother Bonnet preferred to remain at the convent, except
when, as mother superior, she had official business to transact,
and it was Mother Coakley's duty and joy to shepherd the

girls of the school on their occasional visits to town. She was well acquainted in all the shops around the square. She helped the girls to choose gloves and girdles, and chaste perfumes, which she always referred to as "toilet water." The mother superior frowned on the use of perfumes and girdles, but Mother Coakley answered her objections by saying mildly, "God love them, we'll be lucky if that's all the harm they do with their money." During every such visit to town it was customary to drop in at Mr. Feinman's little combination cigar and sports shop on the square and pick up tennis or ping-pong balls, and to cap the afternoon by drinking chocolate frosteds at Fater's corner drugstore. Mother Coakley never ate or drank anything while in town, but she liked to purchase from Mrs. Fater, as unobtrusively as possible, a ten-cent Hershey bar, which she would slip into one of her capacious interior pockets. "Energy food," she would say, making her eyes round and bright. "When you get to be my age . . ."

Mother Coakley's age was one of the few secrets which she had been able to carry over from her girlhood outside the convent, but she must have been past seventy when the mother superior attempted to take a stand on the subject of her playing tennis. Mother Bonnet, who was as lean and slow moving as Mother Coakley was plump and bouncing, had never approved of the latter's athletic activities, and as the years went by it seemed to her less and less appropriate for one of Mother Coakley's age and position to be making of herself, as the mother superior said, "a gross spectacle truly." She had been looking for an excuse to put an end to the display, and the incident in Mr. Feinman's shop was more than enough, she felt, to justify speaking soberly to her.

One winter day, while Mother Bonnet was engaged in her annual skirmish with the tax collector in his office beside the courthouse, Mother Coakley and five or six of the girls spent a strenuous two hours shopping and walking about the town. The girls bought writing paper, cotton stockings, and some sensible, oversize sweaters, and enjoyed the usual chocolate-frosteds at Fater's while Mother Coakley bought, and concealed on her person, the usual ten-cent Hershey bar. Having a few minutes to spare before rejoining Mother Bonnet, they decided to stop off at Mr. Feinman's. Though it was February, the midday sun was always bright and the tennis court was in no worse condition than it would be in June; Mother Coakley and the girls played nearly every afternoon, glorying in their indifference to the calendar. One of the girls had been planning for some time to buy a new racquet, but Mother Coakley and Mr. Feinman had yet to come to terms.

Today, welcoming them, Mr. Feinman swore that he had just what the doctor ordered. He brought out from the dusty shelves at the back of the store, where he kept piled in indiscriminate confusion cases of cigars and baseball mitts, a racquet called the Bluebird Special. "Sweetest little racquet I ever had in the place," Mr. Feinman said, blowing off the dust and hefting the racquet with professional care. Mr. Feinman had never played any game more taxing than pinochle, but he knew how to sell merchandise. He stroked the gut with his fingers. "Like music," he said. "With this racquet is easy wictory. Is steady wictory."

Mother Coakley enjoyed shopping. She particularly enjoyed haggling with her old friend Mr. Feinman. The girls formed an interested half circle about her as she took up the challenge, and a few of the inevitable courthouse loungers gathered at the open door of the shop. Mother Coakley swept this familiar audience with a glance, then, turning to Mr. Feinman, she asked simply, "How much?"

Mr. Feinman held up his hands as if to ward off the wounding mention of money. "For such a racquet? For workmanship like this?"

"How much?" Mother Coakley repeated.

Mr. Feinman consented, with a shrug, to discuss the sordid question. "Ten dollars."

Mother Coakley tapped her broad black belt, making the wooden rosary beads rattle as if in reproach. "Nonsense," she said. When she bargained, she seemed purely French; even her voice took on the accents of Dijon in place of those of Dublin. "It isn't worth five."

Mr. Feinman appealed to the girls behind Mother Coakley and, by extension, to the crowd outside the door. "Five dollars! A work of art for five dollars!" He raised his eyes to the stamped tin ceiling over his head. "May God strike me dead if I didn't pay six dollars for it wholesale. I can—"

"Leave God out of this," Mother Coakley interrupted promptly. "What kind of pagan chatter is that?" She took the racquet from Mr. Feinman's hands and began to execute a few tentative strokes, cutting at and lobbing an imaginary ball. What happened next no one was able afterward to decide. Some people thought that Mr. Feinman had caught sight of the mother superior nearing the entrance to his store and had leaned forward to welcome her. Others thought that he had detected a price tag dangling from the end of the racquet and, being uncertain of what it said, had bent down to retrieve it. In any event, he lowered his head in time to receive, on his left temple, the full force of one of Mother Coakley's savage forehand drives. He dropped in his tracks like a sack of meal, without so much as a moan.

The girl who had intended to buy the racquet began to cry hysterically, "He did it! God did it! God did it!" Mother Coakley knelt beside the motionless figure of Mr. Feinman, her round cheeks looking oddly drawn and pale. "He's not dead," she said sharply, "he can't be. He's breathing. You can see he's breathing." She drew the Hershey bar from her pocket and, breaking off a piece, attempted to force it between Mr. Feinman's lips. At that moment he opened his eyes. In another moment he was on his knees. Slowly, painfully, he pulled himself up. "Is nothing," he said faintly. "Is just a tap."

Mother Coakley had barely begun her apology when another, deeper voice reached her over the heads of the crowd. "*Tais-toi*," said the mother superior. "I am in charge here." She worked her way through the crowd, her habit rustling with authority. She stared first at Mr. Feinman, half crumpled against the counter, and then at Mother Coakley, still armed with the Bluebird Special. "The racquet," she said to Mr. Feinman. "One of the girls is buying this racquet?"

Mr. Feinman nodded.

"How much?"

With the air of a man who knows that it is useless to fight against the power of God, Mr. Feinman said brokenly, "Seven fifty. For a work of art, I will take seven fifty."

The mother superior, fresh from her annual triumph over the tax collector, said, "Very well." She set seven dollars and fifty cents on the counter. Then, turning to the girls, she made a gesture with her hands like that of a farmer's wife scattering hens. "Now, then, *dépêchons*."

The little group was halfway across the square before the mother superior spoke to Mother Coakley. "You and your wretched tennis!" she said bluntly.

Mother Coakley nodded. "I have been thinking it over. I have come to feel that perhaps you are right." She pursed her lips. "Perhaps I am getting old."

"I have wanted you to make your own decision," said the mother superior. She was always glad to be able to temper sternness with magnanimity. Besides, she and Mother Coakley were old friends, and it would be cruel to make her humble herself too far. "It is not that I am angry about this merely. Accidents can happen to anybody."

"No, it was my fault," Mother Coakley said, her voice softening to the brogue. She slipped a piece of the Hershey bar into her mouth. "I shall have to give up my forehand drive. You were right in thinking that I should have done so long ago." Then, despite her best efforts at self-control, her feet began to skip along the asphalt sidewalk. "From now on," she said penitently, "I shall play as badly as I can."

Jean Kerr

WHEN I WAS QUEEN OF THE MAY

Our eight-year-old Johnny was looking for a bottle of cherry soda the other day and, after a brief, despairing survey of the bottles in the refrigerator, he slammed the door shut and asked me, quite seriously, "Mom, were you ever Miss Rheingold?"

I tried to explain to him that consumption of the product, however enthusiastic, was not the real basis for this singular honor. Eventually he grasped the picture, but I could see that it reopened avenues of uncomfortable speculation. Just last winter he had discovered that I couldn't do long division or make divinity fudge. And now this. In a wan effort to regain my lost glamour I told him about the time I was Queen of the May.

I was, at that time, a tall, gangly, giggly thirteen, and a freshman in a seminary for girls. The first hint of the celebrity that was to be mine came when I read on the bulletin board that I must report to the principal's office. I was struck numb with terror, because the only other time I had been thus summoned was after it became known that I was the girl who dared Bunny Ryan to peek over the heavy curtain that separated Sister Mary Olive's bed from all the other beds in the dormitory. (Bunny reported that she had hair all right, but it was very short.) But today I could sense, as soon as I stepped into the office, that I wasn't in serious trouble. For one thing, Mother Claire didn't fix on her pince-nez; a thing she always did when displeased. I don't know whether she simply wanted to get a better look at the offender.

Mother Claire was a saintly old lady of great sweetness and strange sibilance, due, I now suppose, to ill-fitting false teeth.

She never spoke above a whisper, and one could follow her progress down the narrow corridors by the gentle tapping of a cane and a trail of hissing s's. Her standard method of greeting, wherever she encountered us and whatever the occasion, was to raise a powdery white hand and whisper, "S-s-s-softly, young ladies, s-s-softly." Mother was so far from being self-conscious about this impediment that it seemed almost as if she chose her phrases for the difficulties they presented. "Stick-to-it-iveness is necessary for success" she said umpteen times a day, regally unaware of the small storm of whistling consonants that broke about our ears. But such was her air of gentle authority that not one of us would have dreamed of smiling. Nor did we ever mimic her at recess, the way we did Sister Stanislaus, who used to clear her throat three times before she spoke and then say, in hushed, melancholy tones, "A girl who would chew gum will smoke, and a girl who would smoke will drink, and a girl who would drink [pregnant pause]—well, I think you know what that kind of a girl will do." We did, too, or thought we did, and we shuddered deliciously at the fearful prospect.

But Mother was a little island quite removed from our girlish jocularity. On that afternoon, when she said to me, "My dear, I see that you are growing in nature and in grace," I blushed with pleasure quite as if I didn't know that, at one time or another, she had said the same thing to every girl in the school. "Thank you, Mother," I said, curtsying so low that, to my horror, an old yellow comb in a rather forlorn condition fell out of my uniform pocket and clattered to the floor. Mother ignored the comb and my furtive efforts to reclaim it and said, "You will be gratified to learn that your good teachers have chosen you to crown the statue of Our Lady in the grove." I was more than gratified; I was stunned.

In the ordinary course of things there would have been nothing noteworthy about a crowning. Every year on the first of May each class had a private ceremony in which the statues of Our Lady (and there were sometimes two or three in a single classroom) were banked with flowers and crowned with wreaths. Indeed, such was our reputation for zeal in this matter that the girls in a neighboring public school spread the entirely false rumor that we seminarians, in our anxiety to lay laurel on every available plaster head, had inadvertently crowned the bust of Chopin in the music room.

What made this year's crowning a special event was the fact that, for the first time, we were going to crown the massive stone statue that stood in the grove midway between the school and the old folks' home. The statue had been there from time immemorial. (Bunny Ryan said her grandmother remembered it from the time she was a little girl, and since her grandmother had once written to Abraham Lincoln, one sensed that we were in direct contact with antiquity.) What was new, brand new, was the concrete path that wound its way through the rocks and brambles which had hitherto made formal processions out of the question and limited visitors to the shrine to those solitary pilgrims who used to dash out to the grove for an eleventh-hour "Hail Mary" just before a Latin exam.

Now, with the way paved in concrete, all things were possible, and Mother Claire had decreed that this May there would be a formal procession of the entire school, including even the babies in kindergarten who only came half day. All of us were to wear white—pure, stainless white—right down to our toes; and that meant white cotton stockings. This last was a great blow to the seniors (who were by this time wearing silk stockings), and great clusters of them sat on the window sills before class and muttered darkly about certain persons who were "positively *prehistoric*, forcryingoutloud."

Anyway, we knew the great day was nigh and we had all been supposing that Denise Macy would be chosen to do the crowning. She had two aunts in the convent, and it was known that she had obtained a doctor's certificate excusing her from gym only because it was such an affront to her modesty to appear publicly in those blue-serge bloomers. Furthermore, and this was very much to the point, her uncle had donated the eleven hundred dollars for the paving of the path.

But Denise had been passed over and I had been chosen. Why? I simply couldn't understand it. If the selection had been made on the basis of brains, why not Rosemary Schuette, who was so smart that she used to correct the pronunciation of the French teacher and, according to her roommate, frequently wrote torrid love letters to her boy friend in Latin? Alas, I would never have been chosen for my beauty, even though I had been secretly using Stillman's Freckle Cream for two months and felt that my complexion, though temporarily scaly, was much improved. Actually I had a rather realistic view of my physical charms because, as a small child, I had once overheard my mother announce to a friend on the telephone, "Jean's a plain little thing, but we think she's going to be intelligent."

No, it couldn't be brains and it wouldn't be beauty, so what was it, then—goodness? I honestly didn't feel that I was very good, but, falling into the trap of even saints and mystics, I decided that the very fact that I didn't think I was good meant that I was humble. Taking logic a step farther, it had to be granted that a humble person was a good person. It seemed clear enough when you put it that way.

I went home and told my family, but their enthusiasm was a little dampened by the fact that this honor involved the purchase of a white dress. To tell the truth, my mother was still feeling put out because she had had to pay a dressmaker four dollars to make me a sateen Herod costume last Christmas when my entire part consisted in saying fiercely, "Find the Babe, find Him and *kill* Him!"

The day we went dress-hunting my mother swished her way through a whole rack of rather mournful-looking crepe-silk dresses before she called out to the salesgirl, "Surely you have something in size sixteen besides these burial robes?" Eventually the salesgirl produced a white organdy sprinkled all over with red dots. Mother dismissed my anguished cries that it had to be *white*, all white, by saying reasonably, "In the name of God, girl, you want to get another *turn* out of it, don't you?" Quite apart from the red dots, the dress had a little capelet instead of the long sleeves that had been officially prescribed. But my protests were unavailing. Mother's mind was made up—clearly this investment was not going to be the total loss she had supposed—and she said to the salesgirl, "Wrap it up." And to me, "This won't be the first pair of elbows they've seen up there."

On the morning of the great day I crept quaking into the auditorium full of girls in their pristine white dresses, looking and feeling like a bad case of measles. In my heart I fully expected that I would be replaced as crowner. However, when Mother Claire finally caught sight of me and my dots, she merely shut her eyes. A brief look of pain washed over her face. It was the expression you might expect if the chef at Pavillon were asked to contemplate a frozen TV dinner. But she said nothing, and clearly I was to crown as planned.

We assembled out in the driveway, where the nun who taught gym and was thought to have a feeling for organization pulled and pushed us into an orderly file. I was first, accompanied by a tiny girl from the kindergarten who carried the wreath on a silver tray. Then there were four music students with flutes, who were to provide the accompaniment for the hymns. Next came six first-grade girls with baskets of flowers. These were followed by the rest of the school, paired off in twos according to height. There was a slight feeling of uneasiness in the ranks because, owing to the rain yesterday, the dress rehearsal had been held in the gym, and now, with the vast difference in terrain, we felt all turned around. Still, there were no mishaps as the procession wound its slow, solemn way to the shrine.

On arrival, the wreath bearer and I stepped forward while all the other girls fanned out until they had formed three large circles around the shrine. Then, after a warning tweet from the flutes, we sang "'Tis May." I was beginning to feel nervous: the crowning hymn was next.

"'Tis May" proved to be very effective because the five girls who always flatted on the final high C did remember to drop out before the end, as instructed. At last the crowning hymn began. I listened very carefully, for there was a definite place in the lyric indicating the moment when the crowner was to step forward.

It came. The voices rang out high and sweet in the open air, "Oh, Gray-shus Queen of Hea-von, we haste to-oo crown thee-ee now." Then a silence fell—the song was to be continued after the actual crowning—as I picked up the wreath and walked slowly up to the statue.

It was then that I realized, and with a stab to the heart, why I had been chosen. I had been chosen because I was the tallest girl in the school. It was equally clear, as I peered at the massive stone figure looming four or five feet above me, that, tall as I was, I wasn't tall enough. Hoping for further instructions, I shot a look of desperation and panic over to the right, where the nuns were standing in a little clump. But their heads were bowed in benediction, and they seemed totally unaware of the crisis.

Finally Alice McClain, who was class president and a girl of some resourcefulness, signaled the flutes to start up again. Once more the voices sang out, though not, of course, with the same dash: "Oh, Gray-shus Queen of Hea-von, we haste to-oo crown thee-ee now." This time the word "now" seemed a reproach. Was it possible, I wondered, that we would all have to stand here until I grew another six inches?

Just as it seemed fearfully likely that the singing was going to begin for a third time, I remembered Mother Claire's oft-repeated adage, "Desperate diseases require desperate remedies." I took the wreath firmly in my two hands, grasping it like a basketball, and hurled it up onto the head of the statue. For a brief moment it looked as though I had succeeded, for the wreath seemed to be resting firmly on the prongs of the stone crown. But then, slowly and majestically, it slid down until it settled rakishly over one large stone eye. The effect was decidedly disreputable, and there was a hiss of horror from the nuns, as well as a gasp from the girls that quickly degenerated into muffled laughter. The first to be affected were the flutists, who, in an effort to suppress their giggles, had blown spit into their flutes and rendered them useless. The singers, without a flute to guide them, fell silent. The little girl who had borne the wreath burst into tears, and a first-grade flower girl was heard to inquire loudly, "Is it over?"

This was all too much for Mother Claire, who wheeled slowly in her tracks and marched back to the school, followed by the other nuns. Only the gym teacher remained to see that the retreat didn't turn into a rout.

I stood there, bleary with grief, feeling like the captain of a ship that was going down with all aboard. In my own mind I was the innocent victim of fate, but I knew perfectly well that in the minds of the departing nuns I was now an irresponsible defiler of sacred objects. Suddenly I broke out of line and ran down the path until I caught up with Mother Claire. "Oh, Mother," I said, the tears splattering down my cheeks, "I am sorry." Mother put on her pince-nez and looked at me. "Dots," she said sadly, "and now this." "But, Mother—" I explained in what may be the most poignant statement ever made by a thirteen-year-old, "I'm *only* five feet nine."

Even great disasters have a way of being forgotten (who today talks about the Chicago fire?), and pretty soon everybody stopped discussing the crowning and my unworthy part in it. Nevertheless, it was instrumental in changing my life, because two days later I was invited to join the Seven-Uppers. This was a club formed by the seven most popular girls in the school; girls of such incomparable chic and elegance that I had aspired to be one of them only in the dim, helpless way that a copy boy aspires to be managing editor. They had evidently decided that my errors on crowning day were all part of a calculated plan and that, however roughhewn my appearance, I was to be regarded as a cutup and a card. Under these decidedly false pretenses, I joined the Seven-Uppers (there was some talk of changing the name to the Eight-Teens, but that died out). Now I, too, rode in raffish splendor in Dottie Long's maroon roadster after school. And with the others I huddled under the porch at recess and puffed away at an Old Gold. I had come a long way.

Phyllis McGinley

PIPE LINE AND SINKER

"All happy families," said Tolstoi, "resemble one another; every unhappy family is unhappy in its own fashion." Like the generalities of many a lesser sage, the old master's observation has just a trace of truth in it. But not the whole truth. Happiness puts on as many shapes as discontent, and there is nothing odder than the satisfactions of one's neighbor.

Happy families do, however, own a surface similarity of good cheer. For one thing, they like each other, which is quite a different thing from loving. For another, they have, almost always, one entirely personal treasure—a sort of purseful of domestic humor which they have accumulated against rainy days. This humor is not necessarily witty. The jokes may be incomprehensible to outsiders, and the laughter spring from the most trivial of sources. But the jokes and the laughter belong entirely to the families and hence are valuable.

Our own family is probably no gayer than any other group of four people who enjoy each other's company. Still, we have all lived together a long time, and our purse is well supplied. We are forever reaching into it for an anecdote or a recollection.

"Do you remember?" we are continually asking one another.

"Do you remember the picnic when a horse ate our lunch?" "Do you remember how Daddy always dressed up in a white coat and tied a towel around his head when he took our temperatures?" "Do you remember the treasure hunt when everybody forgot where we'd hidden the treasure?"

"Khrushchev" is not a funny name but we never hear it without smiling because that is what Patsy used to call her kerchief when she was four. No one ever remarks that a friend's phone is tied up, without our harking back to Julie's first invented witticism at three. On her toy telephone she was intently dialing a number.

"Hello," she said, "is this the zoo? I want to speak to the lion."

There was a suitable silence. Then, turning to me, she said solemnly, "The lion is busy."

We carefully preserve an Easter card which Patsy drew and painted for us when she was perhaps six. There had been a bad drought that spring, and she had heard much about being sparing with the water supply. The card was a masterpiece of mingled pagan and religious art—rabbits competing with crosses and lilies. It was given to us folded over like a book, and inside she had drawn three balloons, each with its appropriate legend. The first exclaimed, "Happy Easter!" The second announced that "Christ is Risen!" the third said simply, "Save Water."

When the girls were small, we were wary about quoting their sayings. Children do not like to be laughed at. Now, though, they listen greedily when we remind them of unconscious mots from their youth. After all, it is not everyone who can so well sum up the difficulties of virtuous behavior as did our youngest, one night at table. We had been discussing, of all things (and we have always discussed all things), saints. We were claiming favorites among them.

"Which saint would you like best to be?" we asked her, expecting the usual platitudes about the vivacious Teresa or the modest Clare. But our child had a mind of her own.

"Oh," she said firmly, "I'd choose to be a martyr."

We evidently gaped, unbelieving; but she had her reasons marshaled. "You see you only have to be a martyr once."

Some of our stories have a pathetic overtone, like clowns' comedy; and I dare not name which daughter it was who, in second grade, found a dollar bill in a vacant lot on the way home from school. Honest creature that she was, she went up and down the block for an hour, knocking on each door to inquire if anyone had lost a fortune. We live in an evidently scrupulous village, so no one claimed it, and she brought the dollar proudly home to tuck into her bank. After having reassured her that finders of such anonymous wealth were certainly keepers, I asked, "Did you ever find any money before this?"

"Oh, yes," she told me, "once I found a dime under a tree. But I put it back."

No wonder I still worry about that child, even now that she is grown up.

The whole family laughs at me, but not at my jokes, which are rare. What they recall most hilariously are the scrapes I get into through my total lack of mechanical ability. They stopped commenting on the fact that I can't cope with a pencil sharpener or efficiently defrost a refrigerator. They no longer expect me to read a road map or assemble a food chopper. But when I once got locked for hours into my stall shower by pulling the shower door straight through the jamb instead of pushing it properly out—a feat of idiot strength unparalleled by Atlas—it kept them happy as crickets. Particularly when they learned that the handy man from the house next to us had to take the door off its hinges to release me (after someone had mercifully tossed a dressing gown over the transom).

It is my husband, though, whose wit we chiefly savor.

"Here comes Daddy," Julie sang out once when she was a very small girl, waiting at the corner of the hedge for her commuting ancestor. "He brings fun! He brings joy! He brings the paper!"

The compliment with a sting in its tail is our copyrighted brand of family humor. But she was a wise child. She knew her own parent and realized even so early that a cheerful father is as important as he is rare. My husband's jests will not make a Hollywood fortune. Bennett Cerf will never collect his pearls for a column. We collect them, though, and tell our friends with mirth.

I have said in another connection that he is a wit and I stand by that. He is not, however, a raconteur. He has no patience with a manufactured joke and is as likely to betray the point of one by telling it backwards as he is to coin a personal epigram. At those, in our minds, he excels.

"Children should be herded but not seen," he instructed our first nursemaid, quite untruthfully. And he asked me once plaintively why the young must "always run downstairs at the tops of their voices?"

"I have a phenomenal memory," he told a friend of ours who boasted of his steel-trap mind. "I can forget anything."

We do not disdain puns in our limited circle, and we still delight in the social criticism he let fly one evening at the theater. The occasion was a theater benefit for a Worthwhile Charity, but Charity turned out to be very dressy indeed; the orchestra full of white ties and strapless gowns. "Don't you think," he asked me between acts, "that this is rather putting on the underdog?"

And, social or not, I have always cherished his comment on an exceedingly broken-down Victorian chair which I brought home from an auction. "Ah," he said appreciatively, "custom built, no doubt, for the Hunchback of Notre Dame."

Yet it is not his conscious but rather his unpremeditated witticisms which we most greedily collect. For this is a man impatient with the confines of language. Words get in his way, and he meets them head-on, whereat the words obligingly telescope themselves into charming—and apt—portmanteaus. "Dwelf" is ever so much better than "dwarf" or even "elf," we believe, as a description of something gnomish.

"And I fell for it," I heard him murmur after one of the girls had brought off a teasing coup. "Fell for it—pipe line and sinker."

"She's dumb as the ace of spades," he says. Or, "The poor man hasn't a frog's chance."

"I'm so tired I can't keep open," may have a peculiar sound, but how completely fitting it is to describe a state of enervation. We repeat it after him with relish. And we like the way he described a recent acquisition of the household. Dido, our savage but beautiful black cat (named for the Carthaginian queen) was suddenly a mother. My husband rejoiced. He likes cats. He came up from a look at the new nursery, beaming and too enthusiastic to rummage through his vocabulary for the exact word. What he invented was far more expressive. "There she is, proud as Lucifer," he told us, "with that batter of kittens swimming around her." Certainly batter is a splendid term for kittens, and "swimming" which must be a combination of "squirming" and "swarming" has elements of genius.

Our favorite, though, is a simple sentence of gratitude. Someone, one broiling day in the garden, brought him a cold drink.

"Thanks," he exclaimed appreciatively after he had downed it. "That was absolutely a Godsaver."

But if we admire the unexpected rather more than we do his formal japes, we also cherish his description of a certain gossip as "living from mouth to mouth," and of a critic we know as "earning his bread in the sweat of his highbrow." And we never take a motoring trip together that we do not keep in mind his deathless admonition: "We're in a hurry. We haven't time to take a short cut."

If it is true, as he once misquoted Thoreau, that "The mass of men live lives of quiet exasperation," then such recollections as these are the balm.

I have been dipping into the purse at random. The supply is nearly limitless, but many of the happenings which in memory cause us most mirth would not stir anyone but us. These are private treats; privately arrived at. Half of them depend on the joy of recognition. Some of them are esoteric as runes.

Which reminds me of the first time "esoteric" became a family joke. I must explain that, at post-kindergarten age, Pat liked to consider herself never an outsider to anything. "Yes, I know" was the phrase oftenest on her tongue, whether we were discussing modern art, gardening, or child psychology. She was also old enough to be interested in words, but young enough to take them literally.

"Your father makes esoteric jokes," I once remarked at dinner.

"What does *that* mean?" she demanded promptly.

"Esoteric?" I said, always happy to inform the young idea. "Oh, that refers to something private or hidden; something," I went on, "which is known to only a few people."

"Yes, I know," she said automatically.

There was a brief pause, and then came her station announcement. "Yes, I do know. And I know the people too."

Perhaps it's knowing the people which gives a jest its finest flavor.

Evelyn Waugh

TOO, TOO SICK-MAKING

It was clearly going to be a bad crossing.

With Asiatic resignation Father Rothschild, S.J., put down his suitcase in the corner of the bar and went on deck. (It was a small suitcase of imitation crocodile hide. The initials stamped on it in Gothic characters were not Father Rothschild's, for he had borrowed it that morning from the *valet-de-chambre* of his hotel. It contained some rudimentary underclothes, six important new books in *sic* languages, a false beard, and school atlas and gazetteer heavily annotated.) Standing on the deck, Father Rothschild leant his elbow on the rail, rested his chin in his hands, and surveyed the procession of passengers coming up the gangway, each face eloquent of polite misgiving.

Very few of them were unknown to the Jesuit, for it was his happy knack to remember everything that could possibly be learned about everyone who could possibly be of any importance. His tongue protruded very slightly, and, had they not all been so concerned with luggage and the weather, someone might have observed in him a peculiar resemblance to those plaster reproductions of the gargoyles of Notre Dame which may be seen in the shopwindows of artists' colourmen tinted the colour of "Old Ivory," peering intently from among stencil outfits and plasticene and tubes of water-colour paint. High above his head swung Mrs. Melrose Ape's travelworn Packard car, bearing the dust of three continents, against the darkening sky, and up the companionway at the head of her angels strode Mrs. Melrose Ape, the woman evangelist.

"Faith."

"Here, Mrs. Ape."

"Charity."

"Here, Mrs. Ape."

"Fortitude."

"Here, Mrs. Ape."

"Chastity . . . Where is Chastity?"

"Chastity didn't feel well, Mrs. Ape. She went below."

"That girl's more trouble than she's worth. Whenever there's any packing to be done, Chastity doesn't feel well. Are all the rest here—Humility, Prudence, Divine Discontent, Mercy, Justice, and Creative Endeavour?"

"Creative Endeavour lost her wings, Mrs. Ape. She got talking to a gentleman in the train. . . . Oh, there she is."

"Got 'em?" asked Mrs. Ape.

Too breathless to speak, Creative Endeavour nodded. (Each of the angels carried her wings in a little black box like a violin case.)

"Right," said Mrs. Ape, "and just you hold on to 'em tight and not so much talking to gentlemen in trains. You're angels, not a panto, see?"

The angels crowded together disconsolately. It was awful when Mrs. Ape was like this. My, how they would pinch Chastity and Creative Endeavour when they got them alone in their nightshirts. It was bad enough their going to be sick, without that they had Mrs. Ape pitching into them too.

Seeing their discomfort, Mrs. Ape softened and smiled. She was nothing if not "magnetic."

"Well, girls," she said, "I must be getting along. They say it's going to be rough, but don't you believe it. If you have peace in your hearts your stomach will look after itself, and remember if you *do* feel queer—*sing*. There's nothing like it."

"Good-by, Mrs. Ape, and thank you," said the angels; they bobbed prettily, turned about, and trooped aft to the second-class part of the ship. Mrs. Ape watched them benignly, then, squaring her shoulders and looking (except that she really had no beard to speak of) every inch a sailor, strode resolutely forrard to the first-class bar.

Other prominent people were embarking, all very unhappy about the weather; to avert the terrors of seasickness they had indulged in every kind of civilized witchcraft, but they were lacking in faith.

Miss Runcible was there, and Miles Malpractice, and all the Younger Set. They had spent a jolly morning strapping each other's tummies with sticking plaster (how Miss Runcible had wriggled).

The Right Honourable Walter Outrage, M.P., last week's Prime Minister, was there. Before breakfast that morning (which had suffered in consequence) Mr. Outrage had taken twice the maximum dose of a patent preparation of chloral, and losing heart later had finished the bottle in the train. He moved in an uneasy trance, closely escorted by the most public-looking detective sergeants. These men had been with Mr. Outrage in Paris, and what they did not know about his goings on was not worth knowing, at least from a novelist's point of view. (When they spoke about him to each other they called him "the Right *Honourable* Rape," but that was more by way of being a pun about his name than a criticism of the conduct of his love affairs, in which, if the truth were known, he displayed a notable diffidence and the liability to panic.)

Lady Throbbing and Mrs. Blackwater, those twin sisters whose portrait by Millais auctioned recently at Christie's made a record in rock-bottom prices, were sitting on one of the teak benches, eating apples and drinking what Lady Throbbing, with late Victorian chic, called "a bottle of pop," and Mrs. Blackwater, more exotically, called "champagne," pronouncing it as though it were French.

"Surely, Kitty, that is Mr. Outrage, last week's Prime Minister."

"Nonsense, Fanny, where?"

"Just in front of the two men with bowler hats, next to the clergyman."

"It is certainly like his photographs. How strange he looks."

"Just like poor Throbbing . . . all that last year."

". . . And none of us even suspected . . . until they found the bottles under the board in his dressing room . . . and we all used to think it was drink. . . ."

"I don't think one finds *quite* the same class as Prime Ministers nowadays, do you think?"

"They say that only *one* person has any influence with Mr. Outrage . . ."

"At the Japanese Embassy . . ."

"Of course, dear, not so loud. But tell me, Fanny, seriously, do you think really and truly Mr. Outrage has IT?"

"He has a very nice figure for a man of his age."

"Yes, but *his age*, and the bull-like type is so often disappointing. Another glass? You will be grateful for it when the ship begins to move."

"I quite thought we *were* moving."

"How absurd you are, Fanny, and yet I can't help laughing."

So arm in arm and shaken by little giggles, the two tipsy old ladies went down to their cabin.

Of the other passengers, some had filled their ears with cotton wool, others wore smoked glasses, while several ate dry captains' biscuits from paper bags as Red Indians are said to eat snake's flesh to make them cunning. Mrs. Hoop repeated feverishly over and over again a formula she had learned from a yogi in New York City. A few "good sailors," whose luggage bore the labels of many voyages, strode aggressively about smoking small, foul pipes and trying to get up a four of bridge.

Two minutes before the advertised time of departure, while the first admonitory whistling and shouting was going on, a young man came on board carrying his bag. There was nothing particularly remarkable about his appearance. He looked exactly as young men like him do look; he was carrying his own bag, which was disagreeably heavy, because he had no money left in francs and very little left in anything else. He had been two months in Paris writing a book and was coming home because, in the course of his correspondence, he had got engaged to be married. His name was Adam Fenwick-Symes.

Father Rothschild smiled at him in a kindly manner.

"I doubt whether you remember me," he said. "We met at Oxford five years ago at luncheon with the Dean of Balliol. I shall be interested to read your book when it appears—an autobiography, I understand. And may I be one of the first to congratulate you on your engagement? I am afraid you will find your father-in-law a little eccentric—and forgetful. He had a nasty attack of bronchitis this winter. It is a draughty house —far too big for these days. Well, I must go below now. It is going to be rough and I am a bad sailor. We meet at Lady Metroland's on the twelfth, if not, as I hope, before."

Before Adam had time to reply, the Jesuit disappeared. Suddenly the head popped back.

"There is an extremely dangerous and disagreeable woman on board—a Mrs. Ape."

Then he was gone again, and almost at once the boat began to slip away from the quay towards the mouth of the harbour.

Sometimes the ship pitched and sometimes she rolled and sometimes she stood quite still and shivered all over, poised above an abyss of dark water; then she would go swooping down like a scenic railway train into a windless hollow and up again with a rush into the gale; sometimes she would burrow her path, with convulsive nosings and scramblings like a terrier in a rabbit hole; and sometimes she would drop dead like a lift. It was this last movement that caused the most havoc among the passengers.

"Oh," said the Bright Young People. "Oh, oh, oh."

"It's just exactly like being inside a cocktail shaker," said Miles Malpractice. "Darling, your face—*eau de Nil*."

"Too, too sick-making," said Miss Runcible, with one of her rare flashes of accuracy.

Kitty Blackwater and Fanny Throbbing lay one above the other in their bunks, rigid from wigs to toes.

"I wonder, do you think the *champagne* . . . ?"

"Kitty."

"Yes, Fanny, dear."

"Kitty, I think, in fact I am sure I have some sal volatile . . . Kitty, I thought that perhaps as you are nearer . . . it would hardly be safe for me to try and descend . . . I might break a leg."

"Not after *champagne*, Fanny, do you think?"

"But I need it. Of course, dear, *if it's too much trouble?*"

"Nothing is too much trouble, darling, you know that. But now I come to think of it, I remember quite clearly, for a fact, that you did *not* pack the sal volatile."

"Oh, Kitty, oh, Kitty, please . . . you would be sorry for this if I died . . . oh."

"But I saw the sal volatile on your dressing table after your luggage had gone down, dear. I remember thinking, I must take that down to Fanny, and then, dear, I got confused over the tips, so you see . . ."

"I . . . put . . . it . . . in . . . myself. . . . Next to my brushes . . . you . . . beast."

"Oh, Fanny . . ."

"Oh . . . Oh . . . Oh."

To Father Rothschild no passage was worse than any other. He thought of the sufferings of the saints, the mutability of human nature, the Four Last Things, and between whiles repeated snatches of the penitential psalms.

The leader of His Majesty's Opposition lay sunk in a rather glorious coma made splendid by dreams of Oriental imagery—of painted paper houses; of golden dragons and gardens of almond blossoms; of golden limbs and almond eyes, humble and caressing; of very small golden feet among almond blossoms; of little painted cups full of golden tea; of a golden voice singing behind a painted paper screen; of humble, caressing little golden hands, and eyes shaped like almonds and the colour of night.

Outside his door two very limp detective sergeants had deserted their posts.

"The bloke as could make trouble on a ship like this 'ere deserves to get away with it," they said.

The ship creaked in every plate, doors slammed, trunks fell about, the wind howled; the screw, now out of the water, now in, raced and churned, shaking down hatboxes like ripe apples; but above all the roar and clatter there rose from the second-class ladies' saloon the despairing voices of Mrs. Ape's angels in frequently broken unison, singing, singing, wildly, desperately, as though their hearts would break in the effort and their minds lose their reason, Mrs. Ape's famous hymn, "There ain't no flies on the Lamb of God."

The Captain and the Chief Officer sat on the bridge, engrossed in a crossword puzzle. "Looks like we may get some heavy weather if the wind gets up," he said. "Shouldn't wonder if there wasn't a bit of a sea running tonight."

"Well, we can't always have it quiet like this," said the Chief Officer. "Word of eighteen letters meaning carnivorous mammal. Search me if I know how they do think of these things."

Adam Fenwick-Symes sat among the good sailors in the smoking room, drinking his third Irish whiskey and wondering how soon he would feel definitely ill. Already there was a vague depression gathering at the tip of his head. There were thirty-five minutes more, probably longer with the head wind keeping them back.

Opposite him sat a much-travelled and chatty journalist, telling him smutty stories. From time to time Adam interposed some more or less appropriate comment, "No, I say that's a good one," or, "I must remember that," or just, "Ha, Ha, Ha," but his mind was not really in a receptive condition.

Up went the ship, up, up, up, paused and then plunged down with a sidelong slither. Adam caught at his glass and saved it. Then shut his eyes.

"Now I'll tell you a drawing-room one," said the journalist.

Behind them a game of cards was in progress among the

commercial gents. At first they had rather a jolly time about it, saying, "What ho, she bumps," or "Steady, the Bluffs," when the cards and glasses and ash tray were thrown onto the floor, but in the last ten minutes they were growing notably quieter. It was rather a nasty kind of hush.

". . . And forty aces and two-fifty for the rubber. Shall we cut again or stay as we are?"

"How about knocking off for a bit? Makes me tired—table moving about all the time."

"Why, Arthur, you ain't feeling ill, surely?"

"'Course I ain't feeling ill; only tired."

"Well, of course, if Arthur's feeling ill . . ."

"Who'd have thought of old Arthur feeling ill?"

"I ain't feeling ill, I tell you. Just tired. But if you boys want to go on I'm not one to spoil a game."

"Good old Arthur. 'Course he ain't feeling ill. Look out for the cards, Bill, up she goes again."

"What about one all round? Same again?"

"Same again."

"Good luck, Arthur." "Good luck." "Here's fun." "Down she goes."

"Whose deal? You dealt last, didn't you, Mr. Henderson?"

"Yes, Arthur's deal."

"Your deal, Arthur. Cheer up, old scout."

"Don't you go doing that. It isn't right to hit a chap on the back like that."

"Look out with the cards, Arthur."

"Well, what d'you expect, being hit on the back like that? Makes me tired."

"Here, I got fifteen cards."

"I wonder if you've heard this one," said the journalist. "There was a man lived at Aberdeen, and he was terribly keen on fishing, so when he married, he married a woman with worms. That's rich, eh? You see he was keen on fishing, see, and she had worms, see, he lived in Aberdeen. That's a good one, that is."

"D'you know, I think I shall go out on deck for a minute. A bit stuffy in here, don't you think?"

"You can't do that. The sea's coming right over it all the time. Not feeling queer, are you?"

"No, of course I'm not feeling queer. I only thought a little fresh air . . . Christ, why won't the damn thing stop?"

"Steady, old boy. I wouldn't go trying to walk about, not if I were you. Much better stay just where you are. What you want's a spot of whiskey."

"Not feeling ill, you know. Just stuffy."

"That's all right, old boy. Trust Auntie."

The bridge party was not being a success.

"Hullo, Mr. Henderson. What's that spade?"

"That's the ace, that is."

"I can see it's the ace. What I mean you didn't ought to have trumped that last trick not if you had a spade."

"What d'you mean, didn't ought to have trumped it? Trumps led."

"No, they did *not*. Arthur led a spade."

"He led a trump, didn't you, Arthur?"

"Arthur led a spade."

"He couldn't have led a spade because for why he put a heart on my king of spades when I thought he had the queen. He hasn't got no spades."

"What d'you mean, not got no spades? I got the queen."

"Arthur, old man, you *must* be feeling queer."

"No, I ain't, I tell you, just tired. You'd be tired if you'd been hit on the back, same as I was . . . anyway, I'm fed up with this game . . . there go the cards again."

This time no one troubled to pick them up. Presently Mr. Henderson said, "Funny thing, don't know why I feel all swimmy of a sudden. Must have ate something that wasn't quite right. You never can tell with foreign foods—all messed up like they do."

"Now you mention it, I don't feel too spry myself. Damn bad ventilation on these Channel boats."

"That's what it is. Ventilation. You said it."

"You know, I'm funny. I never feel seasick, mind, but I often find going on boats doesn't agree with me."

"I'm like that too."

"Ventilation . . . a disgrace."

"Lord, I shall be glad when we get to Dover. Home, sweet home, eh?"

Adam held on very tightly to the brass-bound edge of the table and felt a little better. He was *not* going to be sick, and that was that; not with that gargoyle of a man opposite, anyway. They *must* be in sight of land soon.

It was at this time, when things were at their lowest, that Mrs. Ape reappeared in the smoking room. She stood for a second or two in the entrance, balanced between swinging door and swinging doorpost; then as the ship momentarily righted itself, she strode to the bar, her feet well apart, her hands in the pockets of her tweed coat.

"Double rum," she said and smiled magnetically at the miserable little collection of men seated about the room. "Why, boys," she said, "but you're looking terrible put out over something. What's it all about? Is it your souls that's wrong, or is it that the ship won't keep still? Rough? 'Course it's rough. But let me ask you this. If you're put out this way over just an hour's seasickness ["Not seasick; ventilation," said Mr. Henderson mechanically] what are you going to be like when you make the mighty big journey that's waiting for us all? Are you right with God?" said Mrs. Ape. "Are you prepared for death?"

"Oh, am I not?" said Arthur. "I 'aven't thought of nothing else for the last half hour."

"Now, boys, I'll tell you what we're going to do. We're going to sing a song together, you and me. ["Oh, God," said Adam.] You may not know it, but you are. You'll feel better for it body *and* soul. It's a song of Hope. You don't hear much about Hope these days, do you? Plenty about Faith, plenty about Charity. They've forgotten all about Hope. There's only one great evil in the world today. Despair. I know all about England, and I tell you straight, boys, I've got the goods for you.

Hope's what you want and Hope's what I got. Here, steward, hand round these leaflets. There's the song on the back. Now all together . . . sing. Five bob for you, steward, if you can shout me down. Splendid, all together, boys."

In a rich, very audible voice Mrs. Ape led the singing. Her arms rose, fell and fluttered with the rhythm of the song. The bar steward was hers already—inaccurate sometimes in his reading of the words, but with a sustained power in the low tones that defied competition. The journalist joined in next and Arthur set up a little hum. Soon they were all at it, singing like blazes, and it is undoubtedly true that they felt the better for it.

Father Rothschild heard it and turned his face to the wall. Kitty Blackwater heard it.

"Fanny."

"Well."

"Fanny, dear, do you hear singing?"

"Yes, dear, thank you."

"Fanny, dear, I hope they aren't holding a *service*. I mean, dear, it sounds so like a hymn. Do you think, possibly, we are *in danger*? Fanny, are we going to be wrecked?"

"I should be neither surprised nor sorry."

"Darling, how can you? . . . We should have heard it, shouldn't we, if we had actually *hit* anything? . . . Fanny, dear, if you like I will have a look for your sal volatile."

"I hardly think that would be any help, dear, since you *saw* it on my dressing table."

"I may have been mistaken."

"You *said* you *saw* it."

The Captain heard it. "All the times I been at sea," he said, "I never could stand for missionaries."

"Word of six letters beginning with ZB," said the Chief Officer, "meaning 'used in astronomic calculations.'"

"Z can't be right," said the Captain after a few minutes' thought.

The Bright Young People heard it. "So like one's first parties," said Miss Runcible, "being sick with other people singing."

Mrs. Hoop heard it. "Well," she thought, "I'm through with theosophy after this journey. Reckon I'll give the Catholics the once-over."

Brian Friel

MY FAMOUS GRANDFATHER

On May 1, 1901, my grandfather, Clarence Parnell Kelly, went on his longest, and what proved to be his last, grand binge. There is no doubt about the date, because May 1 was the traditional opening of the lobster season in Beannafreaghan, and Grandfather should have been at the currach slip that morning with the other fishermen, baiting and weighting his pots; and on that day in that year, my mother, his only child, gave birth to me, her only child. However, Grandfather heard neither the prayer Canon Deeney prayed that God would bless the fishermen's catches nor my first cries at being ushered into the world, because by that time, as was learned later, he had reached Strabane and was selling the horse that had carried him so far to a squint-eyed tinker who saw a chance of an easy bargain.

Exactly thirteen days later, on May 14, Grandfather returned. Again there is no doubt about the date; he missed my christening by a few hours, and he had overshot his usual spree by three days. Up to this, ten days had been his limit, and as each succeeding day passed, Grandmother's righteous resignation turned to concern and then to panic. I have been emphatic about the dates because when he did return—under his own steam, and that, too, was unusual—he carried under his arms two packets which gave my family a claim, for what it's worth, to being pioneers of a sort. He had brought home, soberly and in shy triumph, the first gramophone ever heard in County Donegal.

I heard the story so often from my mother and I grew so close to the man himself, until he was taken from us seven years later, that I can scarcely convince myself that I do not remember the scene, although the baptismal water must still have been damp on my head that evening. Grandmother was sitting on a stool at the door, knitting socks for Taylor the gombeen-man and rocking my cradle with her foot, and Mother was inside the kitchen making the tea for my father, who was due home on the full tide. From our house you could hear the wash of the sea against the slip, and that is why Grandmother did not hear his footsteps coming over the lane. The first thing she knew, he was standing between her and the light, his face wide and expectant like a dog that has done a trick.

Before she had time to utter a word, he said, "It's the miracle of the century! A music box!" Then, with the speed and enthusiasm of an expert salesman, he was down on his knees on the cobbled front and undoing the wrappings of his boxes.

"Where have you been?"

"In Dublin. It's the newest instrument there is; the latest invention. And it plays eight tunes, and if I had four shillings more . . ."

"How much did you spend on that . . . that thing?"

"Fifteen pounds and for nothing at all; brass bands and choirs and melodeons and the finest singers in the whole of Europe, all here at your doorstep."

One packet contained a large mahogany box and the other a horn-shaped instrument. The two women watched in astonishment. Delicately, expertly, he placed on the first record. The machine hissed for a second and went dead.

"The winder! I forgot the winder!"

He inserted the handle in the side and wound up the spring. "Now." He exhaled.

The hissing began again, and then from the mouth of the horn came the high, strained voice of a man being strangled to death. The song he sang was "The Holy City," and in the quiet spring evening, his valiant cries were carried high above the thatched cottage, high above the sound of the waves slapping against the slip, and out across the swollen sea to my father who was pulling for home.

"Jesus and Mary protect us!" screamed Grandmother, blessing herself, and she fled in terror to her bed where she lay
trembling for two days. I began to cry. But across me and the
throttled tenor, Grandfather smiled serenely at my mother
and whispered, "It's a present for the grandchild. A present of
a miracle."

It would probably have been a poor lobster season anyhow,
even if it had been properly tried. Scarcely a day passed but
sudden gales drove in between the twin headlands of Gola and
Cruit and turned the bay into a seething pool of sand and
seaweed. I suppose a brave currach could have put out in the
half-hour calms, laid its pots, and scurried home again.

But the dozen odd fishermen who gathered at the pier each
day and weighed up the prospects with unusual concern for
their safety generally came to the decision that if the seas were
not too heavy now, they soon would be; and since it would be
advisable to hang around in the off-chance that a long calm
might fall, what was more natural for them than go up the
few paces to Clarry Kelly's house and wait there? So that is
what they did. And once there, what was more natural than
that Clarry should produce the machine from the room and
render a few tunes? Perhaps there were short calms, maybe
long calms. Nobody noticed. The magic box held them spell-
bound for hours at a stretch. In the end, the fish agents struck
Beannafreaghan off their calling list altogether, because the
fishermen, as Grandmother said, "had given themselves over
completely to the devil."

The advent of the magic box revolutionized the pattern of
entertainment in our parish. Up to this time, leisure hours
were spent ceilidhing: you dropped in casually on your neigh-
bour and spent the night chatting or playing cards or telling
stories or maybe singing a song or two; or the young people got
their hands on a fiddler and held an informal dance on the
smooth concrete beside the gable of O'Donnell's house. But
now Grandfather's machine became the rage. Within a week
it was obvious that our kitchen could not hold all the people
who turned up every night. So the recital was moved to the

old shed on the pier road, which was used for storing herring boxes.

People came nightly from Bunbeg, from Loughanure, from Fintown, from Dunlewey, even from Tory and Aranmore Islands. They came on sidecars, on bicycles, on horseback, in boats, on foot. And they had about them an atmosphere of excitement and heightened anticipation, because they were more than just concertgoers; they were pioneers, innovators, the first witnesses of a new era, and they were conscious of their privilege. Few of them had ever sat in a concert hall before, and the experience of finding themselves congregated together in orderly rows (fish boxes) and facing an improvised stage (a wooden dray) caused them to react as if they were in church for Sunday Mass; the only comparable situation in their experience. So they listened devoutly and with attention.

It was not until the Farrell brothers turned up drunk one night that they discovered that it would not be sacrilegious to clap, and from then on the applause was tumultuous. Indeed it was not confined to the end. Very often a recording had to be stopped halfway through until some well-held note or some popular line was enthusiastically acclaimed.

Grandfather's fame became countrywide within a month. But in his short time as amateur he had perfected his art as host and entertainer. Gone were the days when he shuffled onto the stage in his thighboots and with his cap well down over his eyes, mumbling a few shy words of introduction about "the lad here," as he deprecatingly called his instrument. He was now the consummate performer. He shaved before a recital and dressed in his Sunday clothes. He never carried the box onto the stage; he walked on two minutes after it had been deposited there by an attendant. Then he would appear himself, and after a very low bow he would announce, "Count yourselves fortunate to be present, people." (This almost biblical preamble puzzled me until my mother explained to me that Grandfather's first tongue was Gaelic and that his English was never very comfortable.) After this solemn opening, Grandfather would then explain as much of the workings of the machine as he thought fit to divulge and then go on to introduce his first record.

He never played a disc without prefacing the performance with an entirely fictitious history of the composer and the music. His only sources were the small labels on the records, but he cunningly utilized every number and letter in his synopsis. He would proclaim, for example: "I now perform a tune which is named 'The Blue Danube.' [He called it Danubey.] This song was written by a poor, humble fisherman called Strauss, a man like ourselves, who earned bread for his family by fishing mackerel in the Danubey Sea. But at night, while his wife knit socks, he wrote songs. This song is a waltz, a little faster than a hornpipe and a little slower than a jig. Mr. Strauss lived in a big city in Europe, and the number of his house was K 31927. His band is called the London Orchestra. Mr. Strauss is now dead. Remember him in your prayers."

This would be greeted with subdued applause, because Grandfather always managed to elevate the recital above the level of mere entertainment; this was something more serious than a haphazard ceilidh.

In all fairness to the man, I must say that he ought to be pardoned his patent affectations and mannerisms, because he sought no recompense for his work: admission to the herring shed was absolutely free and everyone was welcome. I think myself that he saw himself as a sort of apostle. Certainly he left all, fishing boat and lobster pots and his scrap of a farm, to follow his vocation.

So it was only right that he should suffer no material loss. We were never without fish and flour, and when the turf stack got low someone always came along with a new cartload. This new method of living, "charity" she called it, imposed a great strain on Grandmother's virtue. She longed for the old days again when he went on binges and when her vanity had to weather only short, well-spaced storms. Now, she maintained, we were no better than the trick-of-the-loop people, depending for the bite we ate on "all the lilties of the countryside who had no hearth fire to sit at when the dark came."

Soon the day came when the herring shed was too small and when popular demand compelled Grandfather to go on tour. Requests had long been coming in from places as far away as Carrick and Bunaweel—a good, two days' journey even with a change of horses—for the Magic Box Man, as he was now called, to give a concert. Grandfather weighed up these invitations with due solemnity. He was still strictly amateur, so he was at no time influenced by material reward. But he regarded his work with the high seriousness of a poet. If the people of Bunaweel earnestly desired to hear the best artists in all Europe, Grandfather could not find it in his soul to deny them; they had as much right as the people of Beannafreaghan.

So he enlisted the aid of Gusty McCann, the jarvey, to transport him, and of Jimmy the Hen to be his advance agent, and on the first Monday in October, 1901—by good luck, another uncertain day with the result that all the fishermen were there for the send-off—the cortege set off from the pier on the first great tour that was to take them from one end of Donegal to the other.

I have before me now press cuttings from newspapers of that time. These notices were written by what were called "penny-a-line men," local correspondents to the national dailies who were paid a penny a line for their covering of local events. Taken all in all, they could scarcely be called rave notices, but it must be remembered that these correspondents seldom wrote about anything more exciting than the price of heifers at the last fair or the birth of triplet lambs to a sheep. Besides, the gramophone was so startlingly new that thoughtful newsmen were determined to show how thoughtful they were by being restrained and uncommitted.

A typical review is the *Echo*'s:

A capacity audience of 124 persons listened with attention to Mr. Clarence Parnell Kelly's concert in the Hibernian Hall. Mr. Kelly demonstrated the limited capabilities of the gramophone, a machine which, Mr. Kelly claims, can preserve a singing voice or an orchestral piece for all time.

So incoherent were some of the recordings that at times it was difficult to distinguish between the singing voice and the full-scale orchestra. But as Mr. Kelly explained, heavy drapes on the walls and thick carpeting on the floor would have absorbed much of the static electricity in the air. The enjoyment of the evening was greatly enhanced by the highly instructive and deeply scholarly preface which the Music Box Man gave before each item. Sir Hugh Fairley of the *Globe* was among those present.

There cannot have been so much static electricity in Fanad Hall, because the local critic there wrote:

Seldom have the Fanad people had such a feast of good music as on last Friday night when Beannafreaghan's maestro, Clarry Kelly, performed in his magic box. There were to have been eight items on the programme, but so popular was "The Poor Blind Boy" that Mr. Kelly had to perform it nine times in all. Consequently, the paraffin in the lamps had been used up before the last four items could be played, so the concert came to a premature end. Proposing a vote of thanks by candlelight, Mr. J. J. Healey thanked Mr. Kelly for coming so far for nothing at all and for his entertaining and instructive night. The concert ended with the audience and the magic box singing together "The Poor Blind Boy."

The Ballycarrow reporter appeared to have been confused between the prefaces and the performances: "Mr. Kelly's voice was at its best in 'The Holy City' by Clarence Parnell, who was tragically widowed at the age of thirty-three and lived in 15B, Paris."

And the Meenadore correspondent noted briefly: "A dance was held on Sunday night, music provided by Clarry Kelly's amazing gramograph. The proceeds went to charity."

The only two people who begrudged Grandfather his success were Grandmother and Canon Deeney, and both had their reasons. Life had never been more comfortable for Grandmother, but since the moderate luxuries she now enjoyed were not bought out of her sock money or Grandfather's fishing, she could not enjoy them. She still believed in the virtue of a hard and frugal life.

The canon had greater reason for anxiety. He saw his compact little parish becoming the focal point of the county, and while up to this his parishioners had been content with simple pleasures which they indulged in almost under his very eyes, they now began to travel to neighboring parishes for their amusement. He was convinced that Grandfather had started the rot and had set his flock on the steep path to complete hedonism. His Sunday-night dances were no longer attended, because the young people preferred to dance ten or fifteen miles from home, and even Gusty McCann, who had been his private chauffeur for almost twenty-five years, had deserted him for this gadabout Kelly. He prayed for patience and guidance, and his prayers were finally answered—in a way.

The day the canon asked Grandfather to give a concert in Beannafreaghan Parochial Hall was the greatest day of Grandfather's public life. Every artist wants to be acclaimed in his home place, and Grandfather was no exception. The canon's silence had worried him. He had called in the house every Friday morning as usual on his way to the pier for fish for his dinner, but he had never mentioned the gramophone. And on the one occasion when Grandfather brought up the subject, the canon began talking about the price of seed potatoes.

Now there was no longer any doubt about the canon's attitude to the new machine: he was fully in favor of it. Grandfather's work was receiving the blessing of the Church, because he was to give a recital in the parish hall; Canon Deeney himself would sit on the platform beside the magic box, and the proceeds would be used to patch up the roof of the hall, which had been slightly damaged in the December gale.

"It takes culture to know culture," said Grandfather when the canon had left.

"Aye," sniffed Grandmother. "He knows that if you can't beat your enemy, you come to terms with him."

"It will be a big night," said Grandfather, smiling at the ceiling. "I'll get Jimmy the Hen to bill it all over the county, and we'll draw them from Malin Head down to Glencolmcille. We will put a good roof on the hall, all right. We'll put two roofs on it!"

It was a big night, indeed, a bigger night than even the canon or Grandfather could have envisaged. Not only did an admission charge not fetter the people; it seemed to make the attraction even stronger. Within four days the small hall was booked out, but people still came looking for tickets. The hall committee held a meeting extraordinary and decided to put wooden forms along the sides and down the centre aisle. This extra seating was snaffled up in twenty-four hours, and requests still came pouring in.

By now Grandfather's pride and self-importance and a sudden and uncharacteristic greed which had taken hold of the canon had destroyed both men's sense of balance. Against the advice of the committee, they themselves tore down the tiny pay-desk at the door of the hall and persuaded local families to lend kitchen chairs, which they packed into the new floor space. Still not satisfied, they arranged salmon boxes around the stage, called the seats a balcony, and sold them at double the floor prices. Then they had printed a glossy, souvenir program which depicted on the cover Grandfather's mustached face smiling benignly through the horn of his gramophone; they organized a raffle for a half tea set; they arranged for lemonade to be sold during the interval; and they did nothing to kill the rumor which was prevalent that the Poor Blind Boy was to appear in person on the big night.

To this day it is not known how many people squeezed into the hall that night. Some say there were three hundred; some say there were six hundred. But the truth is that not even the hall committee ever knew. The receipts amounted to £39 7s. 6d., but that is no lead, because mothers who had lent chairs were given free tickets for their families and, in the last five minutes before the scheduled opening, stewarding arrangements at the door collapsed completely, with the result that seven currachloads from Innisman got in without paying anything and, in that last minute melee, all the urchins who had been hanging around the porchway nipped smartly inside.

From where they stood at the edge of the platform, the canon and Grandfather could see row after row of happy, upturned faces. When they turned around to the salmon-box balcony behind them, row after row of happy faces beamed down at them. The canon was flushed with delight.

"Clarence," he said, "this night will go down in the annals of the Church."

At the stroke of eight, the canon held out his hands for silence and began his introductory speech. He was not a man of few words at any time, but that night he lost control of himself altogether. He welcomed the audience, reminded them of their Christian heritage, explained to them the need for raising money to repair the roof, told them of his future building plans, asked them to be patient while he explained his scheme for renovating the graveyard, and only when he had to raise his voice to be heard above the hum of conversation around him, did he introduce the star of the night, Clarence Kelly. Grandfather bowed in acknowledgement, and the audience clapped in relief.

But the canon was only warming up. He then delivered a eulogy on the Kellys, on all the fishermen of Beannafreaghan, on all the good people of Beannafreaghan parish. Indeed, he had noble and generous things to say about all the people of Donegal—for that matter, about all the people of Ireland. And that brought him back to their Christian heritage and somehow to an explanation for their being gathered together that night, united as they were in brotherly love and in true Christian charity.

By this time the patrons were scarcely polite. They shuffled in their seats and waved to one another across the floor. Those behind the canon mimed messages to friends in the body of the hall. The mood of anticipation was quickly leaking away.

"Start the music! Start the music!"

The drunken voice of one of the Farrell brothers interrupted the canon just as he was saying "I am proud of you all tonight." He held out his hands for silence.

"Certainly. Certainly. I have held things up long enough," he said. "Well now, ladies and gentlemen, I have pleasure in introducing again Beannafreaghan's Magic Box Man, our own Clarry Kelly." And Grandfather took the center of the stage.

The night had begun badly: Grandfather was long enough a trouper to know that. His audience was bored, restless, uncomfortable and hot. He would have to dispense with the preface to the first record and try to win the people back with a rousing martial air. He played a Sousa march. Before it was half over he knew it was a mistake. He should have begun with something more personal—a song, a song with a story.

As soon as the Sousa march ended, he took off the record and put on "A Wandering Minstrel." The reaction was no better. The whispered talk had grown into normal conversation. Now Grandfather felt panic; he knew he was losing control. But he decided that when the second record would end, he would tell them the interesting story of Strauss. That would get them on their toes.

"Ladies and gentlemen," he began when the time came, "I wish to tell you about the gentleman who wrote the next song."

"Where's the Blind Boy? We want the Blind Boy!" Farrell's unmistakable voice rose from somewhere near the door.

"Mr. Strauss was a poor, humble fisherman like ourselves, and he wrote a song called . . ."

"The Blind Boy! Where is he? Where is he?"

Farrell was already attracting a following. A few supporters throughout the hall clapped him encouragingly.

". . . called 'The Blue Danube,' which Mr. Strauss wrote while his wife knit socks for . . ."

"Is he here? The Blind Boy! The Blind Boy!"

The cry was taken up by the urchins and some of the Innisman people.

The canon sprang to his feet. "If these interruptions continue I will call the whole concert off," he shouted. "Let there be no more of it."

"We want the Blind Boy. Where is he hiding? Bring him out! Bring him out!"

"Throw those men out," roared the canon.

"The Blind Boy! We want him! We want him!" chorused Farrell and his followers.

"While his wife knit socks, he wrote songs," Grandfather went on thinly.

"Remove that drunkard! Remove him!"

"We were frauded! The Blind Boy's not here!"

"Quiet! Silence! Throw him out!"

"The Blind Boy! The Blind Boy! The Blind Boy!"

"The street number of his house was K 319—"

"Out with the drunkards! Out! Out!"

The hall was suddenly split into several opposing groups, and each group began calling support for its candidate.

"Let Kelly speak! Give him a chance to speak!"

"Farrell's right. We were frauded. Where is the Blind Boy?"

"Respect for the priest, boys. Respect for the priest. Let the priest have his say."

The canon begged for quiet, but his voice was not heard beyond the first three rows. The Farrell followers at the back, although perhaps few, gave the impression of strength by chanting in unison. "The Blind Boy! The Blind Boy! The Blind Boy!"

"Mr. Strauss lived in Europe and the number of his—"

"Tramps! Drunkards! Island savages! Wastrels!" screamed the canon. "Throw them out! Throw them out!"

". . . faster than a hornpipe and a little slower than—"

"Out! Out, I say! Out with them! Out! Out!"

"The Blind Boy! The Blind Boy! The Blind Boy!"

There are conflicting reports of what happened next. My mother maintained that the patrons in the salmon-box balcony, answering the canon's war cry, leaped down from their stage and made for the troublemakers at the door. On the other hand, my grandmother swore that the people at the back came rushing up the hall "like lions heading for Christians."

Anyhow, both factions met in the middle of the hall and there the fight began. Strictly speaking, it was not a fight at all, but the women's screaming and the children's crying gave the authenticity of a real riot. It is true that some men from Gweedore took advantage of the pushing and shoving to punch and kick the men from Kincasslagh, and it is true that the Kincasslagh men defended themselves vigorously, but that was a traditional feud and had nothing to do with the concert. Of course there were chairs broken and some windows, but all in all there was more sound than fury. No one was seriously hurt. It was only when the police arrived to clear the hall that the real damage was discovered: the gramophone and records were in smithereens, and Grandfather was crouched over the remnants, trying to shield them with his body.

No one had ever heard a price put on the damage done to Beannafreaghan Parochial Hall that night. The only person who knew was the canon, and he, poor man, still had his pride. The following morning he went quietly round to the thirty families who had lent him chairs and paid them ten shillings each even though some of them had recovered broken bits during the night. That afternoon he sat outside what had once been his fine hall and refunded ticket money to anyone mean enough to claim it.

"Sure, hadn't we far better fun the way it was?" Maggie Square is supposed to have said to him. But even then he did not open his mouth. One of the Duggans fixed the windows, and a firm of contractors from Letterkenny made new seats and repaired the roof. During the months the work was being carried out the canon could not trust himself to speak any Sunday.

Grandfather went back to his fishing. There were people who said that the experience aged him, made him anticlerical, embittered him, made him soft in the head, killed him. All lies. He was the same man he had always been—slightly quieter perhaps, but more reliable now that he no longer went on the tear. He was now past the age of using his own boat, so he worked along with my father, and they had almost six years together before the old man passed away one Easter Sunday morning when the tide began to ebb.

I do not remember the wake or the funeral, although I had begun school at the time. But I remember bringing a bottle of cold tea and a couple of slices of bread wrapped in newspaper to my father the first day he went out alone with the pots. He was sitting on the pier wall, tying a flat stone to the bottom of the cage, and his eyes were wet and red. He was embarrassed because I had seen him.

"It was the old fella," he said gruffly. "When we would be setting the pots out there beyond the point, he would go through that rigmarole he used to give out when he put on one of them silly old records of his. Is that all the bread she gave you?"

I left Beannafreaghan during World War I and I was not back again until 1945. They have a fine new harbor there now with motorboats hitting up against its side. The old house has gone and the herring shed, but the hall still stands foursquare on top of its hillock. I asked the young girl in the post office about it.

"Which hall do you mean?" she asked. "The dance hall or Kelly's hall?"

"The old parochial hall," I explained.

"Oh, yes. Kelly's. We have films there three nights a week."

"Kelly's? Who calls it Kelly's?"

"I never heard it called anything else," she said. "Somebody called Kelly probably built it long ago."

I did not enlighten her, but it occurred to me that that gives us a second claim, for what it's worth, to fame.

Katherine Mansfield

TAKING THE VEIL

It seemed impossible that anyone should be unhappy on such a beautiful morning. Nobody was, decided Edna, except herself. The windows were flung wide in the houses. From within there came the sound of pianos, little hands chased after each other and ran away from each other, practicing scales. The trees fluttered in the sunny gardens, all bright with spring flowers. Street boys whistled, a little dog barked; people passed by, walking so lightly, so swiftly, they looked as though they wanted to break into a run. Now she actually saw in the distance a parasol, peach coloured, the first parasol of the year.

Perhaps even Edna did not look quite as unhappy as she felt. It is not easy to look tragic at eighteen when you are extremely pretty, with the cheeks and lips and shining eyes of perfect health. Above all, when you are wearing a French-blue frock and your new spring hat trimmed with cornflowers. True, she carried under her arm a book bound in horrid black leather. Perhaps the book provided a gloomy note, but only by accident; it was the ordinary library binding. For Edna had made going to the library an excuse for getting out of the house to think, to realize what had happened, to decide somehow what was to be done now.

An awful thing had happened. Quite suddenly, at the theatre last night, when she and Jimmy were seated side by side in the dress circle, without a moment's warning—in fact, she had just finished a chocolate almond and passed the box to him again—she had fallen in love with an actor. But—fallen—in—love . . .

The feeling was unlike anything she had ever imagined before. It wasn't in the least pleasant. It was hardly thrilling.

Unless you can call the most dreadful sensation of hopeless misery, despair, agony, and wretchedness thrilling. Combined with the certainty that if that actor met her on the pavement after, while Jimmy was fetching their cab, she would follow him to the ends of the earth at a nod, at a sign, without giving another thought to Jimmy or her father and mother or her happy home and countless friends again. . . .

The play had begun fairly cheerfully. That was at the chocolate-almond stage. Then the hero had gone blind. Terrible moment! Edna had cried so much she had to borrow Jimmy's folded, smooth-feeling handkerchief as well. Not that crying mattered. Whole rows were in tears. Even the men blew their noses with loud trumpeting noises and tried to peer at the program instead of looking at the stage. Jimmy, most mercifully dry eyed—for what would she have done without his handkerchief?—squeezed her free hand and whispered "Cheer up, darling girl!" And it was then she had taken a last chocolate almond to please him and passed the box again. Then there had been that ghastly scene with the hero alone on the stage in a deserted room at twilight, with a band playing outside and the sound of cheering coming from the street. He had tried—ah! how painfully, how pitifully—to grope his way to the window. He had succeeded at last. There he stood holding the curtain while one beam of light, just one beam, shone full on his raised, sightless face, and the band faded away into the distance. . . .

It was—really, it was absolutely—oh, the most—it was simply—in fact, from that moment Edna knew that life could never be the same. She drew her hand away from Jimmy's, leaned back, and shut the chocolate box for ever. This at last was love!

Edna and Jimmy were engaged. She had had her hair up for a year and a half; they had been publicly engaged for a year. But they had known they were going to marry each other ever since they walked in the Botanical Gardens with their nurses, and sat on the grass with a wine biscuit and a piece of barley-sugar each for their tea. It was so much an accepted thing that Edna had worn a wonderfully good imitation of an engagement ring out of a cracker all the time she was at school. And up till now they had been devoted to each other.

But now it was over. It was so completely over that Edna found it difficult to believe that Jimmy did not realize it too. She smiled wisely, sadly, as she turned into the gardens of the Convent of the Sacred Heart and mounted the path that led through them to Hill Street. How much better to know it now than to wait until after they were married! Now it was possible that Jimmy would get over it. No, it was no use deceiving herself; he would never get over it! His life was wrecked, was ruined; that was inevitable. But he was young. . . . Time, people said, Time might make a little, just a little difference. In forty years when he was an old man, he might be able to think of her calmly—perhaps. But she—what did the future hold for her?

Edna had reached the top of the path. There under a new-leafed tree, hung with little bunches of white flowers, she sat down on a green bench and looked over the Convent flower beds. In the one nearest to her there grew tender stocks with a border of blue, shell-like pansies, with at one corner a clump of creamy freesias, their light spears of green crisscrossed over the flowers. The Convent pigeons were tumbling high in the air, and she could hear the voice of Sister Agnes who was giving a singing lesson. "*Ah-me*," sounded the deep tones of the nun, and *Ah-me*, they were echoed. . . .

If she did not marry Jimmy, of course, she would marry nobody. The man she was in love with, the famous actor— Edna had far too much common sense not to realize that would never be. It was very odd. She didn't even want it to be. Her love was too intense for that. It had to be endured, silently; it had to torment her. It was, she supposed, simply that kind of love.

"But, Edna!" cried Jimmy. "Can you never change? Can I never hope again?"

Oh, what sorrow to have to say it, but it must be said. "No, Jimmy, I will never change."

Edna bowed her head; and a little flower fell on her lap, and the voice of Sister Agnes cried suddenly "Ah-no," and the echo came, Ah-no. . . .

At that moment the future was revealed. Edna saw it all. She was astonished; it took her breath away at first. But, after all, what could be more natural? She would go into a convent. . . . Her father and mother do everything to dissuade her, in vain. As for Jimmy, his state of mind hardly bears thinking about. Why can't they understand? How can they add to her suffering like this? The world is cruel, terribly cruel! After a last scene when she gives away her jewellery and so on to her best friends—she so calm, they so brokenhearted—into a convent she goes. No, one moment. The very evening of her going is the actor's last evening at Port Willin. He receives by a strange messenger a box. It is full of white flowers. But there is no name, no card. Nothing? Yes, under the roses, wrapped in a white handkerchief, Edna's last photograph with, written underneath:

THE WORLD FORGETTING, BY THE WORLD FORGOT.

Edna sat very still under the trees; she clasped the black book in her fingers as though it were her missal. She takes the name of Sister Angela. Snip! Snip! All her lovely hair is cut off. Will she be allowed to send one curl to Jimmy? It is contrived somehow. And in a blue gown with a white headband Sister Angela goes from the convent to the chapel, from the chapel to the convent with something unearthly in her look, in her sorrowful eyes, and in the gentle smile with which she greets the little children who run to her. A saint! She hears it whispered as she paces the chill, wax-smelling corridors. A saint! And visitors to the chapel are told of the nun whose voice is heard above the other voices, of her youth, her beauty, of her tragic life, tragic love. "There is a man in this town whose life is ruined. . . ."

A big bee, a golden, furry fellow, crept into a freesia, and the delicate flower leaned over, swung, shook; and when the bee flew away it fluttered still as though it were laughing. Happy, careless flower!

Sister Angela looked at it and said, "Now it is winter." One night, lying in her icy cell she hears a cry. Some stray animal is out there in the garden, a kitten or a lamb or—well, whatever little animal might be there. Up rises the sleepless nun. All in white, shivering but fearless, she goes and brings it in. But next morning, when the bell rings for matins, she is found tossing in high fever . . . in delirium . . . and she never recovers. In three days all is over. The service has been said in the chapel, and she is buried in the corner of the cemetery reserved for the nuns, where there are plain crosses of wood. Rest in Peace, Sister Angela. . . .

Now it is evening. Two old people leaning on each other come slowly to the grave and kneel down sobbing, "Our daughter! Our only daughter!" Now there comes another. He is all in black; he comes slowly. But when he is there and lifts his black hat, Edna sees to her horror his hair is snow white. Jimmy! Too late, too late! The tears are running down his face; he is crying *now*. Too late, too late! The wind shakes the leafless trees in the churchyard. He gives one awful bitter cry.

Edna's black book fell with a thud to the garden path. She jumped up, her heart beating. My darling! No, it's not too late. It's all been a mistake, a terrible dream. Oh, that white hair! How could she have done it? She has not done it. Oh, heavens! Oh, what happiness! She is free, young, and nobody knows her secret. Everything is still possible for her and Jimmy. The house they have planned may still be built, the little solemn boy with his hands behind his back watching them plant the standard roses may still be born. His baby sister . . . But when Edna got as far as his baby sister, she stretched out her arms as though the little love came flying through the air to her, and gazing at the garden, at the white sprays on the tree, at those darling pigeons blue against the blue, and the convent with its narrow windows, she realized it now at last for the first time in her life—she had never imagined any feeling like it before—she knew what it was to be in love, but—in—love!

G. K. Chesterton

THE EXTRAORDINARY CABMAN

On the day that I met the strange cabman I had been lunching in a little restaurant in Soho in company with three or four of my best friends. My best friends are all either bottomless skeptics or quite uncontrollable believers, so our discussion at luncheon turned upon the most ultimate and terrible ideas. And the whole argument worked out ultimately to this: that the question is whether a man can be certain of anything at all. I think he can be certain, for if (as I said to my friend, furiously brandishing an empty bottle) it is impossible intellectually to entertain certainty, what is this certainty which it is impossible to entertain? If I have never experienced such a thing as certainty I cannot even say that a thing is not certain. Similarly, if I have never experienced such a thing as green I cannot even say that my nose is not green. It may be as green as possible for all I know, if I have really no experience of greenness. So we shouted at each other and shook the room; because metaphysics is the only thoroughly emotional thing. And the difference between us was very deep, because it was a difference as to the object of the whole thing called broadmindedness or the opening of the intellect. For my friend said that he opened his intellect as the sun opens the fans of a palm tree, opening for opening's sake, opening infinitely forever. But I said that I opened my intellect as I opened my mouth, in order to shut it again on something solid. I was doing it at the moment. And as I warmly pointed out, it would look uncommonly silly if I went on opening my mouth infinitely, forever and ever.

Now when this argument was over, or at least when it was cut short (for it will never be over), I went away with one of my companions, who in the confusion and comparative insanity of a General Election had somehow become a member of Parliament, and I drove with him in a cab from the corner of Leicester Square to the members' entrance of the House of Commons, where the police received me with a quite unusual tolerance. Whether they thought that he was my keeper or that I was his keeper is a discussion between us which still continues.

It is necessary in this narrative to preserve the utmost exactitude of detail. After leaving my friend at the House, I took the cab on a few hundred yards to an office in Victoria Street which I had to visit. I then got out and offered him more than his fare. He looked at it, but not with the surly doubt and general disposition to try it on which is not unknown among normal cabmen. But this was no normal, perhaps no human, cabman. He looked at it with a dull and infantile astonishment, clearly quite genuine. "Do you know, sir," he said, "you've only given me 1s. 8d.?" I remarked with some surprise, that I did know it. "Now you know, sir," said he in a kindly, appealing, reasonable way, "you know that ain't the fare from Euston." "Euston," I repeated vaguely, for the phrase at that moment sounded to me like China or Arabia. "What on earth has Euston got to do with it?" "You hailed me just outside Euston Station," began the man with astonishing precision, "and then you said—" "What in the name of Tartarus are you talking about?" I said with Christian forbearance. "I took you at the southwest corner of Leicester Square." "Leicester Square," he exclaimed, loosing a kind of cataract of scorn, "why we ain't been near Leicester Square today. You hailed me outside Euston Station and you said—" "Are you mad, or am I?" I asked with scientific calm.

I looked at the man. No ordinary dishonest cabman would think of creating so solid and colossal and creative a lie. And this man was not a dishonest cabman. If ever a human face was heavy and simple and humble, and with great big blue eyes protruding like a frog's, if ever (in short) a human face was all that a human face should be, it was the face of that resentful and respectful cabman. I looked up and down the street; an unusually dark twilight seemed to be coming on. And for one second the old nightmare of the skeptic put its finger on my nerve. What was certainty? Was anybody certain of anything? Heavens! To think of the dull rut of the skeptics who go on asking whether we possess a future life. The exciting question for real skepticism is whether we possess a past life. What is a minute ago, rationalistically considered, except a tradition and a picture? The darkness grew deeper from the road. The cabman calmly gave me the most elaborate details of the gesture, the words, the complex but consistent course of action which I had adopted since that remarkable occasion when I had hailed him outside Euston Station. How did I know (my skeptical friends would say) that I had not hailed him outside Euston? I was firm about my assertion; he was quite equally firm about his. He was obviously quite as honest a man as I, and a member of a much more respectable profession. In that moment the universe and the stars swung just a hair's-breadth from their balance, and the foundations of the earth were moved. But for the same reason that I believe in fixed character of virtue, the reason that could only be expressed by saying that I do not choose to be a lunatic, I continued to believe that this honest cabman was wrong, and I repeated to him that I had really taken him at the corner of Leicester Square. He began with the same evident and ponderous sincerity. "You hailed me outside Euston Station, and you said. . . ."

And at this moment there came over his features a kind of frightened transfiguration of living astonishment, as if he had been lit up like a lamp from the inside. "Why, I beg your pardon, sir," he said. "I beg your pardon. I beg your pardon. You took me from Leicester Square. I remember now. I beg your pardon." And with that this astonishing man let out his whip with a sharp crack at his horse and went trundling away. The whole of which interview before the banner of St. George, I swear, is strictly true.

I looked at the strange cabman as he lessened in the distance and the mists. I do not know whether I was right in fancying that although his face had seemed so honest there was something unearthly and demoniac about him when seen from behind. Perhaps he had been sent to tempt me from my adherence to those sanities and certainties which I had defended earlier in the day. In any case it gave me pleasure to remember that my sense of reality, though it had rocked for an instant, had remained erect.

Lucile Hasley

JEANMAIRE, JEANMAIRE!

Jeanmaire, the French *première ballerina*, recently enriched my newspaper reading by consenting—in a Hollywood press interview—to give her views on American wives. I would like to quote, if you can bear it, one of the more fascinating paragraphs:

"I think life here in America is easier for women because they are more spoiled," Jeanmaire said, after a thoughtful pause. "I don't say they deserve it, but they get so much attention from their husbands."

After a thoughtful pause on *my* part, I hauled out my typewriter. Jeanmaire, Jeanmaire! I said to myself, as I settled down at the keyboard. I got some news for you, honey.

To begin with, Jeanmaire, I think you should know that Indiana (which is one of the fifty states and legally recognized as part of America) was settled by strong pioneer stock—from which I spring—and that the womenfolk underwent great hardships. Toiling slowly across the flat, open plains in ox-pulled covered wagons—dodging the Indians—depending on wild game and fish for sustenance—cooking over open kettles—fighting off buzzards with only their sunbonnets—

It was a hard life, Jeanmaire, and I want you to know that things out here in Indiana haven't improved too much. For instance, my husband—and you'll be hearing more about *him* shortly—still feels the need to supplement our food supply by fishing. You'll also, shortly, be hearing more about *that*. Anyway, I could put up with this rude, primitive existence—as what real woman couldn't?—if only my husband still loved me and showered me with little attentions. Something more, you know, than just bringing home bluegills and an occasional bullhead.

My first intimation, Jeanmaire, that my husband—after sixteen years of married life—was no longer madly in love with me, came in the summer of '51. We were at Lake Wawasee, and I remember the scene perfectly. We were out on the lake; the sun was just sinking; the water lapped gently against the rowboat.

"This is the end," said my husband as he jabbed a fat, juicy catalpa worm that squirted in all directions onto my fishing hook. "Sixteen years of this is enough! Starting as from now on, sister, you're going to bait your own hook."

I paled. "You can't do this to me," I said in a husky voice. "I'll fight you in every court in the land. I'll carry this thing to the Supreme Court if necessary. I'll—"

He handed me my pole. "You wouldn't have a chance," he said. "Pah, a grown woman who won't bait her own hook! Why, there isn't a judge in the country who wouldn't uphold me. I'll bet they'd even award me the children without so much as—Hey! *Don't* throw your line right on top of mine. Throw it out on the other side."

So. *Now* he didn't want me on his side of the boat, our fishing lines intimately tangled together. This was what came, I thought—as I crouched, brooding and sullen, over my pole— of trying to be a Good Sport and pretending to share my husband's passion for fishing. Why, only three weeks before (unfortunately, Jeanmaire, college professors get long summer vacations), I'd found myself in the wilds of Canada . . . being a Good Sport in a 2 × 4 cabin with a kerosene lamp and outdoor plumbing . . . while it rained for three solid days. And for why? To catch fish. To provide sustenance.

Oh, sure, I'd heard some people refer to fishing as a "sport" and as "recreation," but I'd never put any stock in the report. Surely, men were only driven to fishing because of sheer hunger? Nor did I put any stock in that highly suspicious endorsement of fishing that was attributed to Allah: "Allah does not deduct from the allotted time of man those hours spent in fishing." It was certainly shortening *my* life span and I felt that Allah—

"For heaven's sake," said my husband, interrupting my Mohammedan meditations, "*why* don't you ever check your bait?"

I gave a little jump. "Oh, I'm sure it's fine," I said nervously. The catalpa worm had probably dissolved long ago, but who was I to hasten the evil hour when I'd have to replace it? "Look," I went on, to divert him, "isn't the sunset pretty now? I mean, all that purple and pink—"

"Look at your bait!" he roared, sounding like Captain Queeg in *The Caine Mutiny*. "Don't you *want* to catch a fish?"

And have it eat up the worm? Don't be silly, I thought. Besides, catching a fish now might be dangerous on other grounds. Now that my husband no longer loved me, the next edict would probably be that I even had to—oh, he couldn't, *he couldn't*. What man, with even a shred of chivalry, would expect a woman to remove the hook from the bloody and mutilated jaws of a flapping fish? No man. Except possibly my husband?

I quelled the mutiny rising in my bosom long enough to take a quick look at the worm. Something resembling about an inch of white slimy sewing thread, No. 60, still remained. I plopped it quickly back in the water and reported, cheerily, that the worm was in fine condition. Practically as good as new, no sense in wasting—

"I saw it!" roared Captain Queeg. "Pull in that line! Now, what do you want to try putting on? A night crawler, a grubworm, or a catalpa?"

(Jeanmaire, I would like to repeat that I come from pioneer stock. I can, without batting an eyelash, kill spiders, cockroaches, June bugs, and centipedes. I once, at a snake farm outside of Washington, even stroked a drugged boa constrictor. I just can't stand *worms*, is all.)

"What," I now said in a faint voice, "is the skinniest thing you have? What has—*urp*—the fewest insides to ooze out?"

He handed me a six-inch slimy night crawler, and one look at it and you'd know why it crawled at *night*, that immediately slithered around my index finger and fell to the bottom of the boat. I could see it, between the boards, sluicing around in a half inch of dirty water. Drowning, I hoped.

"Rescue it," ordered Captain Queeg sternly. "We don't waste worms aboard this boat. Besides, you didn't even *try* to hang onto it."

Beads of sweat were standing out on my brow by the time I once again had the worm in starting position. "Now, don't act as if you were threading a needle," said this stranger in the boat with me. (Twenty-four hours earlier he had been a kind and loving husband. Now, I felt, he would stop at nothing.) "Insert the hook firmly—NO!—not in the middle; near the end—all right, now!—slide the worm onto the hook—then in and out—that's it—keep pushing. So what if part of him *has* fallen off? You've still got a good four inches to work with— keep pushing—"

"I think it's dead by now," I said after several centuries had glided by. "Can I quit? Can we go home now?"

For answer, Queeg picked up the tin of worms, gave it a knowing thump with his hand, and extracted a fresh one.

Three night crawlers, two catalpa worms, and one grub- worm later (the grub having proved the winning number) I had baited a hook to suit Queeg. That is, the worm—although badly mangled—was still alive and was, all things considered, in much better shape than I. *I*—that spoiled American wife, smothered under with attentions from my husband—barely had the strength to lean over the boat and rinse the greenish- white entrails off my hands.

Jeanmaire, I had—in the past half hour—come close (or as close as I would ever come) to what is referred to as the Dark Night of the Soul. The stark stripping of the senses—the con- viction of utter abandonment by both God and man—the yearning for death. Generally, I know, a soul so tested has *already* been raised to a rare degree of sanctity but—don't be too fast, Jeanmaire, in ruling me out. I'd been married, remember, for sixteen years to you-know-who.

Besides, God's ways are inscrutable. He can, in the acid testing of the spirit, use either worms or nails. And I humbly think that I, with my very first night crawler, shot through the purgative stage like Halley's comet. That I slowly emerged into the illuminative stage when I realized, on facing the catalpa, that *my* will no longer counted. That I soared into the unitive stage when I—abandoned, in darkness, with the grubworm— still did not openly rebel against God. God, who had invented worms.

I just rebelled, is all, against my husband. (A human being acting like a worm is even more despicable than the real article.) Anyway, Jeanmaire, I want you to know that I haven't baited a hook since that dark and dreadful scene at Wawasee. Translated, this means that I haven't gone fishing since. *This*, translated, means that this past summer—and high time, too —I took off on a two weeks' solo vacation: a vacation that is openly referred to, in these parts, as The Mrs. Hasley Mutiny.

But *you* understand, don't you, Jeanmaire? I mean, after all I'd gone through? How my old pioneer bones needed the healing rays of the sun on the Maryland seashore? How I needed, to restore my spirit, to be with kind and loving friends?

My husband, of course, stayed home and took care of the three children. But don't get any ideas, Jeanmaire, that he was *spoiling* me. I admit it was quite decent of him and all that, but—and this makes all the difference, as any woman knows—he didn't think of it *all by himself*. I had to suggest it.

"It may be true," I said in a darkly suggestive voice, "that the family that prays together, stays together, but as for the family that *fishes* together—well, it just might work vice versa. You know what I mean?"

Queeg seemed to know.

"And before I die," I went on in a voice that implied it wouldn't be long, "I'd like a vacation that's a *housewife's* idea of a vacation. I would like to stay in a swishy hotel and wallow in luxury. I would like to be as unpioneerish as possible. I would like, above all, to be a Poor Sport for two solid weeks and have nothing whatsoever to do with fish. Except, maybe, with a fork."

Well, Jeanmaire, it was a lovely vacation. I flew to New York and spent a week with kind and loving friends in Scarsdale, roughing it on a wooded estate that resembled Hyde Park. The only hardship I faced in Scarsdale was in having to carry my own tray out to the terrace one evening for a buffet supper. But what could I do, Jeanmaire? I mean, the hostess was my dearest friend, and I could scarcely refuse—even though it meant hiking from the kitchen through the butler's pantry through the dining room, living room, and television room *before* reaching the terrace. The living room, of course, was the worst stretch. All *it* needed, it was so long, was some bowling pins at one end.

Exhausted by all this hiking, I rather dreaded—to tell the truth—the long trek to the seashore, but it wasn't so bad. At least, it wasn't so bad as the ox-pulled covered-wagon treks of my ancestors. You see, Jeanmaire, my friends and I flew down to Maryland in the company's private plane: complete with picture windows, swivel chairs, a lounge, and a telephone. So, having taken my usual Dramamine pill before flying, I was in fairly good condition when we reached the Colonial Hotel (which couldn't have been *more* Colonial unless it had the Potomac flowing by instead of the boardwalk) and quite ready for the rigorous week ahead. Such as sauntering down to the dining room every morning and picking up a menu with GOOD MORNING! embossed on the cover. (So like home.) And then, after stowing away a five-course breakfast, calling out to the beach boy to please—and step fast, boy!—set up our striped umbrellas and chairs for the day's lolling on the beach.

The only disturbing note in this Paradise enow was the news from home. My husband was now, it seemed, maltreating our daughters. "I've been taking them fishing every night out at the Notre Dame lake," he wrote. "You should see them bait their own hooks by now. *They're* really good sports."

Resolutely ignoring this subtle jibe, I proceeded—after, that is, I'd dropped into the Star-of-the-Sea Church to pray for my daughters—to enjoy my Poor Sport vacation with even more vigor. That is, lolling a little harder. I even, Jeanmaire, began to take a rather strange delight in the occasional fishy smell that came in on the evening sea breezes. It was a cozy live-and-let-live feeling, knowing the fish were safe and happy in their proper element and I in mine.

And then, Jeanmaire, it happened. We were lolling on the beach one fine afternoon when my dear friend's husband suddenly reared up on one elbow. "Hey, look!" he cried, his face and voice positively aglow. "Here comes a marlin boat! Three blue flags and one red. That means they've got three marlin aboard, Lu, and someone has earned a Good Sport Medal."

"What d'ya mean, Good Sport Medal?" I said, with a faint flicker of interest, or maybe just because I was sensitive on the point.

"You get this little medal, see, if you catch a marlin and are good enough sport to throw it back in the sea. Come on," he said, dragging us to our feet, "let's go down and watch them land."

By the time we got there the three marlin were strung up on exhibition, although the three Poor Sports, the cads who insisted on keeping their haul, had understandably slunk away. I gazed at the eight-foot, sword-nosed, aluminum-skinned marlin with a speculative eye. What, I asked myself, would I ever want with a marlin? What could be *less* painful than to part with the creature; heave it right overboard again? *Ergo*, what *easier* way could I possibly find to redeem myself in my husband's eyes, and be hailed as a Good Sport?

For the first time in my life, Jeanmaire, I felt a burning urge to go fishing. There was just one thing that bothered me. "Would the man," I asked, "bait the hook for me?"

"*Certainly!*" was the answer. "In fact, he'd insist on it. Of course, Lu, it costs seventy-five dollars to hire the yacht."

The price seemed negligible—a mere pittance, in fact, to pay the nice man for baiting my hook—and look what I'd have! A little medal. Surely, I reasoned, my husband would be only too happy to wire me the necessary money.

Jeanmaire, I know you'll find this hard to believe—even after all I've told you about Queeg—but he flatly refused to send me a penny. He wasn't, he said, paying any seventy-five dollars so I could throw a fish overboard.

So now you know, Jeanmaire. I mean, how American husbands really treat their wives and how—when it comes to a seventy-five-dollar showdown—you can't say much for their sportsmanship, either.